Bond

Verbal Reasoning

Assessment Papers

9–10 years
Book 2

Malcolm Thomas

Nelson Thornes

Published in 2012 by:
Nelson Thornes Ltd
Delta Place
27 Bath Road
CHELTENHAM
GL53 7TH
United Kingdom

12 / 10 9 8 7 6 5 4 3 2

A catalogue record for this book is available from the British Library

ISBN 978 1 4085 1589 1

Page make-up by Tech Set Ltd

Printed and bound in Spain by GraphyCems

Before you get started

What is Bond?

This book is part of the Bond Assessment Papers series for verbal reasoning, which provides a **thorough and progressive course in verbal reasoning** from ages six to twelve. It builds up reasoning skills from book to book over the course of the series.

What does this book cover and how can it be used to prepare for exams?

Verbal reasoning questions can be grouped into four distinct groups: sorting words, selecting words, anagrams, coded sequences and logic. *Verbal Reasoning 9-10 Book 1* and *Book 2* practise a wide range of questions appropriate to the age group drawn from all these categories. The papers can be used both for general practice and as part of the run up to 11+ and other selective exams. One of the key features of Bond Assessment Papers is that each one practises **a very wide variety of skills and question types** so that children are always challenged to think – and don't get bored repeating the same question type again and again. We believe that variety is the key to effective learning. It helps children 'think on their feet' and cope with the unexpected: it is surprising how often children come out of verbal reasoning exams having met question types they have not seen before.

What does the book contain?

- **15 papers** – each one contains 65 questions.
- **Tutorial links throughout** - 📖 – this icon appears in the margin next to the questions. It indicates links to the relevant section in *How to do ... 11+ Verbal Reasoning*, our invaluable subject guide that offers explanations and practice for all core question types.
- **Scoring devices** – there are score boxes in the margins and a Progress Chart on page 60. The chart is a visual and motivating way for children to see how they are doing. It also turns the score into a percentage that can help decide what to do next.
- **Next Steps Planner** – advice on what to do after finishing the papers can be found on the inside back cover.
- **Answers** – located in an easily removed central pull-out section.

How can you use this book?

One of the great strengths of Bond Assessment Papers is their flexibility. They can be used at home, in school and by tutors to:
- set **timed formal practice** tests – allow about 40 minutes per paper. Reduce the suggested time limit by five minutes to practise working at speed.
- provide **bite-sized chunks** for regular practice
- **highlight strengths and weaknesses** in the core skills
- identify **individual needs**
- set **homework**
- follow a complete 11+ preparation strategy alongside *The Parents' Guide to the 11+* (see overleaf).

It is best to start at the beginning and work though the papers in order. If you are using the book as part of a careful run-in to the 11+, we suggest that you also have two other essential Bond resources close at hand:

How to do … 11+ Verbal Reasoning: the subject guide that explains all the question types practised in this book. Use the cross-reference icons to find the relevant sections.

The Parents' Guide to the 11+: the step-by-step guide to the whole 11+ experience. It clearly explains the 11+ process, provides guidance on how to assess children, helps you to set complete action plans for practice and explains how you can use *Verbal Reasoning 9-10 Book 1* and *Book 2* as part of a strategic run-in to the exam.

See the inside front cover for more details of these books.

What does a score mean and how can it be improved?

It is unfortunately impossible to predict how a child will perform when it comes to the 11+ (or similar) exam if they achieve a certain score on any practice book or paper. Success on the day depends on a host of factors, including the scores of the other children sitting the test. However, we can give some guidance on what a score indicates and how to improve it.

If children colour in the Progress Chart on page 60, this will give an idea of present performance in percentage terms. The Next Steps Planner inside the back cover will help you to decide what to do next to help a child progress. It is always valuable to go over wrong answers with children. If they are having trouble with any particular question type, follow the tutorial links to *How to do … 11+ Verbal Reasoning* for step-by-step explanations and further practice.

Don't forget the website…!

Visit www.bond11plus.co.uk for lots of advice, information and suggestions on everything to do with Bond, the 11+ and helping children to do their best.

Paper 1

Underline the pair of words most similar in meaning.

     Example   come, go   <u>roam, wander</u>   fear, fare

1 test, exam   learn, read   science, mathematics

2 melt, fade   dirty, clean   rot, decay

3 drink, water   eat, consume   join, attract

4 hard, rough   black, red   light, pale

5 extend, enlarge   side, back   easy, late

Underline the two words, one from each group, which are the most opposite in meaning.

     Example   (dawn, <u>early</u>, wake)   (<u>late</u>, stop, sunrise)

6 (once, then, here)   (never, open, now)

7 (large, hairy, wild)   (tiny, untidy, cold)

8 (stretch, easy, loose)   (pull, tight, take)

9 (awake, dark, hollow)   (solid, open, confused)

10 (second, minute, first)   (hour, third, final)

Complete the following sentences by selecting the most sensible word from each group of words given in the brackets. Underline the words selected.

     Example   The (<u>children</u>, books, foxes) carried the (houses, <u>books</u>, steps) home from the (greengrocer, <u>library</u>, factory).

11 The (farmer, teacher, shopkeeper) asked the (men, sheep, children) to eat their (shoes, lunches, flowers) sensibly.

12 Don't (try, remember, forget) (swimming, jumping, running) in such a strong (puddle, tide, night).

13 Why are those (boats, trees, cows) standing (huddled, wide, near) together in the (shop, ground, field)?

14 The (team, colour, home) scored a (peach, ball, goal) to win the (last, match, run).

15 James (rubbed, used, whisked) the (jumper, dessert, pencil) with a (hose, pound, fork).

Underline the two words which are made from the same letters.

B 7

Example TAP PET <u>TEA</u> POT <u>EAT</u>

16 SHADES   SHADOW   SHIELD   DASHES   SHINES

17 STARS   TEARS   STATE   TEASE   RATES

18 PEARS   STEER   SPEAR   PLEAT   TREAT

19 SHOVE   FLASH   FLESH   SHAVE   SHELF

20 LATER   STEEL   TRAIL   STEAL   LEAST

5

Find the four-letter word hidden at the end of one word and the beginning of the next word. The order of the letters may not be changed.

B 21

Example The children had bats and balls.   _sand_

21 He decided to have breakfast early that morning.   _____

22 The garage mechanic repaired her new car promptly.   _____

23 'Don't I get a hello any more?' asked Mum.   _____

24 He put a larger dynamo onto the old bicycle.   _____

25 This was a radical move for Professor Furey.   _____

5

Find the letter which will end the first word and start the second word.

B 10

Example peac (<u>h</u>) ome

26 mal (__) scape

27 pou (__) eat

28 see (__) ade

29 tea (__) ota

30 soa (__) ure

5

Find and underline the two words which need to change places for each sentence to make sense.

B 17

Example She went to <u>letter</u> the <u>write</u>.

31 The motor lake roared across the calm boat.

32 You thought that she couldn't hear I.

33 The mechanic was repaired by the car.

34 Where is you think she do going?

35 The caged sea roared like a angry lion.

5

Fill in the missing letters. The alphabet has been written out to help you.

A B C D E F G H I J K L M N O P Q R S T U V W X Y Z

Example   AB is to CD as PQ is to <u>RS</u>

36 JK is to LM as RS is to _____

37 GE is to DB as AY is to _____

38 EF is to HI   as KL is to _____

39 T5 is to V7 as X9 is to _____

40 XX is to YA as BB is to _____

5

Which one letter can be added to the front of all of these words to make new words?

Example   _c_are   _c_at   _c_rate   _c_all

41 ___old   ___read   ___ait   ___rand

42 ___and   ___old   ___oup   ___hare

43 ___otion   ___ay   ___ould   ___ore

44 ___our   ___outh   ___oung   ___ell

45 ___live   ___bate   ___bout   ___mend

5

Fill in the crosswords so that all the given words are included. You have been given one letter as a clue in each crossword.

46

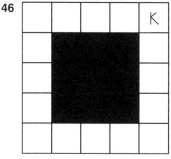

tiles, shark, start, knees

47

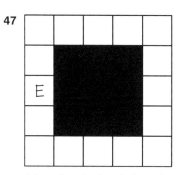

tries, fresh, front, heads

48

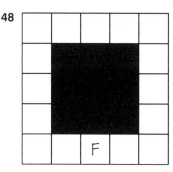

tufts, elves, aloft, above

49

empty, round, rupee, daisy

50

grand, gruel, dough, laugh

If the code for TRAVEL is $ * : £ − &, what are the codes for the following words?

51 REAL   _____

52 TEAR   _____

53 LEAVE   _____

If the code for TRAIN is @ < ? > !, what do these codes stand for?

54 @ ? <   _____

55 @ ? > ! @   _____

Underline the one word which **cannot be made** from the letters of the word in capital letters.

	Example STATIONERY	stone	tyres	ration	<u>nation</u>	noisy
56	DETAILED	late	dated	laid	leaded	tamed
57	SUPERVISE	revise	revue	vipers	every	serve
58	COMPLICATED	laced	matted	calmed	placed	malice
59	MANAGEMENT	games	agent	magenta	meant	game
60	TIDEMARK	taker	dream	dimmer	marked	armed
61	ESTRANGE	gears	snare	grates	earns	groan

A football match is being held in London. To get there, you would have to travel 12 km from Wiston. If you lived in Bridgeworth you would have to go 4 km further than from Wiston but 6 km less than from Hambury. From Fettle it is only half the distance to London that it would be from Hambury.

62 Which town is closest to London?   _____

63 Which town is furthest from London?   _____

64 How far is Bridgeworth from London? _____

65 How much further from London is Wiston than Fettle? _____

4

Now go to the Progress Chart to record your score! Total 65

Paper 2

Underline the two words in each line which are most similar in type or meaning.

B 5

Example <u>dear</u> pleasant poor extravagant <u>expensive</u>

1 withdraw build retrain construct demolish

2 destroy remove put place lie

3 attempt adjust leave reveal try

4 starting grave thoughtful ending serious

5 easy correct wrong complex effortless

5

Underline the pair of words most opposite in meaning.

B 9

Example cup, mug coffee, milk <u>hot, cold</u>

6 flat, even false, true strange, wild

7 continuous, ended allowed, admitted flaky, dry

8 quick, swift plain, elegant hunch, guess

9 wet, damp truth, honesty criticise, praise

10 cured, improved full, complete well, ill

5

Underline the two words, one from each group, that go together to form a new word. The word in the first group always comes first.

B 8

Example (hand, <u>green</u>, for) (light, <u>house</u>, sure)

11 (good, high, flat) (friend, out, mate)

12 (cold, wet, at) (put, tack, pie)

13 (for, try, down) (lawn, late, sake)

14 (on, out, way) (fold, cry, lie)

15 (left, in, far) (vest, way, out)

5

5

Find the three-letter word which can be added to the letters in capitals to make a new word. The new word will complete the sentence sensibly.

B 22

Example   The cat sprang onto the MO.   <u>USE</u>

16–17 Jane's BHER told her that his cat had FOLED him to school that day. _____ _____

18–20 Her CLASSE told Seena she should TELEPH
her mother to come and collect her IMMEDILY.   _____ _____ _____

5

Find the four-letter word hidden at the end of one word and the beginning of the next word. The order of the letters may not be changed.

B 21

Example   The children had bats and balls.   <u>sand</u>

21 He reached the deadline in time.   _____

22 The rusty old door opened with a scary creak.   _____

23 Tara reminded her mother that Monday was a holiday.   _____

24 On Sunday the hen would stop laying eggs.   _____

25 The prisoner shouted his plea several times.   _____

5

Change the first word into the last word, by changing one letter at a time and making a new, different word in the middle.

B 13

Example   CASE   <u>CASH</u>   LASH

26 PUSH _____ POST

27 REAR _____ SEAT

28 LAST _____ HOST

29 FINE _____ MINT

30 STAR _____ SNAG

5

Complete the following sentences by selecting the most sensible word from each group of words given in the brackets. Underline the words selected.

B 14

Example   The (<u>children</u>, books, foxes) carried the (houses, <u>books</u>, steps) home
from the (greengrocer, <u>library</u>, factory).

31 When will we (land, address, arrive) in our (fresh, artistic, holiday) (conservatory, resort, canvas)?

32 Which (way, man, frog) do we (eat, go, hunt) to get to the (theatre, lunch, flower)?

33 The (quiet, hungry, learner) driver kept (eating, speeding, stalling) the car's (supper, engine, wheels).

34 In the (hungry, spotted, haunted) (bush, castle, wagon) lived an evil (spirit, brick, bathroom).

35 In (art, mathematics, history) we learn about (dance, football, graphs) and (television, numbers, drawing).

Choose two words, one from each set of brackets, to complete the sentences in the best way.

> **Example**   Smile is to happiness as (drink, <u>tear</u>, shout) is to (whisper, laugh, <u>sorrow</u>).

36 Monday is to Wednesday as (Tuesday, Thursday, Sunday) is to (Monday, Wednesday, Saturday).

37 Flight is to aircraft as (walk, trial, sailing) is to (car, ship, automobile).

38 Rim is to plate as (picture, shore, water) is to (lake, painting, drink).

39 Uncertain is to sure as (tired, restricted, grateful) is to (late, unlimited, trained).

40 Trivial is to insignificant as (considerate, unstable, trembling) is to (generous, prudent, unkind).

Fill in the crosswords so that all the given words are included. You have been given one letter as a clue in each crossword.

fried, hatch, death, fetch

story, diary, grind, goats

elect, brown, night, bathe

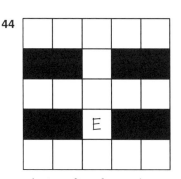

irate, after, forge, later

45

chest, metre, mocha, pleat

Give the missing numbers in the following sequences.

Example 2 4 6 8 10 <u>12</u>

46 62 58 __ 50 46 42

47 6 7 9 12 16 __

48 1 5 3 __ 5 9

49 15 25 20 30 __ 35

50 1 2 4 8 __ 32

B 23

If the code for BALLISTIC is < > ? ? £ % X £ +, what are the codes for the following words?

51 BALLS _____

52 LIST _____

53 STAB _____

What do these codes stand for?

54 £ ? ? _____

55 + > ? ? _____

B 24

Underline the one word in each group which **cannot be made** from the letters of the word in capital letters.

Example STATIONERY stone tyres ration <u>nation</u> noisy

56 REMAINDER mined denim rider married drained

57 WORKMANSHIP shrimp prism hawks plank sharp

58 TELEVISION version invites seven event list

59 ARRANGEMENT remnant manager anger garment nearest

60 PERSONAL snare polar salon plain loans

B 7

Anna supports France and England. Liam supports Wales and England. Malik does not support Scotland but supports Wales. Donna supports Scotland, England and Brazil. David hates football.

B 25

61 How many teams do Donna and Malik support together? _____

62 Which country has the most supporters? _____

2

Eleanor lives 5 km from school. Michael lives nearest to school. Francesca lives 2 km closer than Eleanor, who lives 4 km further from the school than Michael. Robert lives 1 km further than Michael.

B 25

63 Who lives furthest from school? _____

64 How much nearer to school is Michael than Francesca? _____

2

Charlotte is five years older than Lianne, who is four years younger than Lily. Lily is one year older than Ellie, who is three years older than Jessica. Ellie is 10.

B 25

65 Which two girls are twins? _____

1

Now go to the Progress Chart to record your score!   Total ◯ 65

Paper 3

Underline the word in the brackets closest in meaning to the words in capitals.

B 5

Example	UNHAPPY	(unkind death laughter <u>sad</u> friendly)
1	PULL, TUG	(drop drag eat kick boat)
2	WASP, BEETLE	(butterfly horse salmon snake mouse)
3	POMEGRANATE, TOMATO	(sprout lettuce apple onion beetroot)
4	CONTRACT, PACT	(agreement code shrink invitation signature)
5	WALES, FINLAND	(London Essex Leeds Russia Kent)

5

Underline the two words, one from each group, which are the most opposite in meaning.

B 9

Example   (dawn, <u>early</u>, wake)   (<u>late</u>, stop, sunrise)

6 (wonder, love, try)   (find, heat, hate)

7 (hard, fine, soft)   (furry, effortless, light)

8 (reject, refill, waste)   (conserve, rubbish, useful)

9 (fair, honest, closed)   (just, truthful, dark)

10 (reduce, infinite, counted) (endless, hourly, limited)

5

Find the letter that will end the first word and start the second word.

B 10

Example   peac (<u>h</u>) ome

11 fus (——) dge

12 mat (——) lse

13 coa (——) imb

14 int (——) ath

15 shu (——) umb

5

Find a word that can be put in front of each of the following words to make new, compound words.

B 11

Example   CAST   FALL   WARD   POUR   <u>DOWN</u>

16 KNOB   STEP   MAT   BELL   _____

17 BY   STILL   POINT   PIPE   _____

18 KEEPER   TABLE   SCALE   SHARE   _____

19 PAPER   AGENT   REEL   FLASH   _____

20 ACHE   BURN   BEAT   FELT   _____

5

Find the four-letter word hidden at the end of one word and the beginning of the next word. The order of the letters may not be changed.

B 21

Example   The children had bats and balls.   <u>sand</u>

21 She is at her wits' end with her homework.   _____

22 Please empty your pockets before putting your trousers in the laundry. _____

23 The biscuits are at the back of the cupboard.   _____

24 As it hurtled down the street, the car turned and spun round. _____

25 The fiercest of dinosaurs lived throughout the cretaceous age. _____

5

Find and underline the two words which need to change places for each sentence to make sense.

B 17

Example   She went to <u>letter</u> the <u>write</u>.

26 Who have could dreamed that it would come true?

27 After computer I like to play on my school.

28 Two plus four is two.

29 It is never steal to right.

30 Where in the China is world?

5

Give the missing numbers in the following sequences.

B 23

Example 2   4   6   8   <u>10</u>

31   15   12   9   6   ___

32   11   33   ___   77   99

33   128   64   32   ___   8

34   5   8   12   17   ___

35   54   45   36   ___   18

5

Fill in the crosswords so that all the given words are included. You have been given one letter as a clue in each crossword.

B 19

36

their, enter, paint, price

37

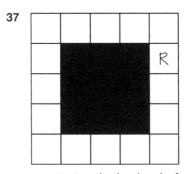

event, stand, shade, draft

38

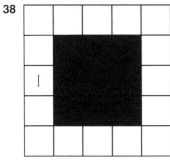

reign, thorn, faint, flair

39

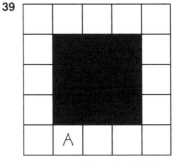

tardy, truth, taint, holly

40

magic, flown, attic, ghost

5

Choose two words, one from each set of brackets, to complete the sentences in the best way.

> **Example**   Smile is to happiness as (drink, <u>tear</u>, shout) is to (whisper, laugh, <u>sorrow</u>).

41 First is to last as (late, second, aged) is to (fine, young, final).

42 Shirt is to cloth as (sock, shoe, earring) is to (string, grass, leather).

43 Past is to present as (once, lessen, increase) is to (multiply, last, first).

44 Halve is to double as (change, third, force) is to (remain, second, unravel).

45 Constant is to always as (final, unique, copied) is to (original, late, related).

If the code for C H A N G E A B L E is written ! ' £ $ % ^ £ & * ^, what are the codes for the following words?

46 HANG   _____

47 ABLE   _____

What do these codes stand for?

48 & £ * *   _____

49 & ^ £ $ _____

50 £ ! ' ^   _____

Underline the one word which **cannot be made** from the letters of the word in capital letters.

> **Example**   STATIONERY   stone   tyres   ration   <u>nation</u>   noisy

51 PORCELAIN   plain   clear   price   race   relay

52 COMMERCIAL   cream   realm   alert   moral   rice

53 GRINDSTONE   tried   stored   noted   rested   nesting

54 INVESTIGATE   tease   sting   ingest   testing   starve

55 SIGNATURE   agent   ignore   rents   great   surge

In football Alison can play in goal or in defence. Soraya can play in midfield or in attack. James never plays in goal, but can play in other positions. Lena can play in midfield or in attack. Kim can play in any position. Geeta can play in defence or midfield.

56 Who can play in any position except in goal?   _____

57 Which two children play the same positions?   _____

58 If Alison is ill, who will play in goal?   _____

59 How many children can play in attack? _____

60 How many children can play in midfield but not defence? _____

B 16

Rearrange the muddled letters in capitals to make a proper word. The answer will complete the sentence sensibly.

Example A BEZAR is an animal with stripes. ZEBRA

61 We put one foot in front of the other when we LWKA. _____

62 NALIF is another word for last. _____

63 We are taught a SENLOS. _____

64 I have TPSNE all my pocket money. _____

65 REELTTS make up the alphabet. _____

Now go to the Progress Chart to record your score! **Total** 65

Paper 4

Underline the two words, one from each group, which are closest in meaning.

B 3

Example (race, shop, <u>start</u>)   (finish, <u>begin</u>, end)

1 (push, trace, flash)   (take, shove, fly)

2 (weed, creep, weep)   (rush, cry, flip)

3 (spoil, try, mend)   (ignore, waste, repair)

4 (refuse, control, retry)   (manage, oppose, enjoy)

5 (uphold, agree, stay)   (refuse, support, change)

Find the three-letter word which can be added to the letters in capitals to make a new word. The new word will complete the sentence sensibly.

B 22

Example The cat sprang onto the MO. USE

6 We had chocolate PUDG for dessert. _____

7 It is a SE that it is raining, as we wanted to go out. _____

8 We had MALADE on our toast. _____

9 She decided to SPRLE marshmallows on her hot chocolate. _____

10 The store AGER asked the customers if she could help them. _____

Find the letter that will end the first word and start the second word.

Example peac (h) ome

11 mas (___) nit

12 sal (___) ach

13 tin (___) ard

14 pri (___) ask

15 man (___) dit

Find a word that can be put in front of each of the following words to make new, compound words.

Example CAST FALL WARD POUR <u>DOWN</u>

16 DOORS SIDE LINE FIT _____

17 WORKS MONGER CLAD WARE _____

18 MAN FLAKE DROP BALL _____

19 BALL LASH SHADOW LID _____

20 MAN CARD CODE BOX _____

Find the four-letter word hidden at the end of one word and the beginning of the next word. The order of the letters may not be changed.

Example The children had bats and balls. *sand*

21 Each inspector must be well trained. _____

22 The tired old man came along the street slowly. _____

23 The train the *Golden Pride* approached slowly along the track. _____

24 He had certainly made advances with his handwriting. _____

25 He applied for his library card because he liked reading. _____

Change the first word of the third pair in the same way as the other pairs to give a new word.

Example bind, hind bare, hare but, <u>hut</u>

26 pit, tip rat, tar tub, _____

27 made, mace fade, face ride, _____

28 part, start pale, stale peer, _____

29 seal, sale meal, male fear, _____

30 flea, leaf stag, tags plea, _____

Complete the following sentences by selecting the most sensible word from each group of words given in the brackets. Underline the words selected.

B 14

Example The (<u>children</u>, books, foxes) carried the (houses, <u>books</u>, steps) home from the (greengrocer, <u>library</u>, factory).

31 The fastest (girl, cheetah, car) in the (shop, school, forest) came (last, once, first) in the 100 metre race.

32 I wonder if we will be (calling, eating, taking) a spelling (cry, test, man) next (cake, week, word).

33 (Charging, Flying, Climbing) mountains can be (trusting, easy, dangerous) in poor (weather, hunger, air).

34 Daisy (felt, wondered, knew) whether she should (try, fall, rub) to call for (food, excellence, assistance).

35 (Always, Never, Forever) forget to (start, make, brush) your (feet, hands, teeth) before going to bed.

5

Find and underline the two words which need to change places for each sentence to make sense.

B 17

Example She went to <u>letter</u> the <u>write</u>.

36 Once upon a woman there lived an old time.

37 There been have two assemblies today.

38 The baby was crying the through all night.

39 This is the very last tell I am going to time you!

40 I wonder that he decided to do why.

5

Complete the following expressions by filling in the missing word.

B 15

Example Pen is to ink as brush is to _paint_

41 Three is to third as nine is to _____.

42 England is to English as France is to _____.

43 Month is to year as decade is to _____.

44 High is to low as up is to _____.

45 Land is to dry as sea is to _____.

5

Give the missing letters and numbers in the following sequences. The alphabet has been written out to help you.

B 23

A B C D E F G H I J K L M N O P Q R S T U V W X Y Z

Example CQ   DQ   EP   FP   _GO_   _HO_

46   C   F   I   L   __   __

47   DC   DD   DE   DF   __   __

48	A3	B5	C7	___	E11	___
49	YB	WD	___	SH	QJ	___
50	___	___	RQ	NM	JI	FE

5

Solve the problems by working out the letter codes. The alphabet has been written out to help you.

B 24

A B C D E F G H I J K L M N O P Q R S T U V W X Y Z

Example   In a code SECOND is written as UGEQPF. How would you write THIRD?   <u>VJKTF</u>

51 In a code PRINCE is written as NPGLAC. How would you write NICE?   _____

52 In a code ICON is written as HBNM. What does SVHF stand for?   _____

53 In a code APE is written as BRH. How would you write LOOK?   _____

54 In a code FEEL is written as IHHO. How would you write WAIT?   _____

55 In a code RICE is written as VMGI. How would you write DOG?   _____

5

Ann and Rhinffrew like lemonade. Peter likes cola, but not lemonade. Siobhan likes orange and cola. Angus only likes cola.

B 25

56 Which is the most popular drink?   _____

57 Which person likes the most types of drink?   _____

2

Chester is west of Birmingham, but east of Bangor. Shrewsbury is south of Chester.

B 25

58 Which town is furthest west?   _____

1

Three years ago Simeon was three years old. In four years' time he will be twice the age of his sister Sophie. Their mother is five times Simeon's age now. Their father is two years older than their mother.

B 25

59 How old will Sophie be in four years' time?   _____

60 How old was their mother three years ago?   _____

61 How old is their father now?   _____

62 How much older is Simeon than Sophie?   _____

4

If $a = 1$, $b = 3$, $c = 4$, $d = 6$, $e = 10$, find the answer to these calculations:

B 26

63 $e - d =$ _____

64 $d \div b =$ _____

65 $a + b + c =$ _____

3

Now go to the Progress Chart to record your score!   Total   **65**

16

Paper 5

1–5 Look at these groups of words.

H	C	G
Homes	Containers	Games

Choose the correct group for each of the words below. Write in the letter.

skipping ___   basket ___   Cluedo ___   urn ___

den ___   flat ___   cup ___   lodge ___

casket ___   snakes and ladders ___

Find the three-letter word which can be added to the letters in capitals to make a new word. The new word will complete the sentence sensibly.

Example   The cat sprang onto the MO.   USE

6 CARS are my favourite vegetables.   _____

7 The nurse put some OINTT on the wound.   _____

8 The WING machine was full of dirty clothes.   _____

9 The old lady DEDED on her carer to help her get out of bed.   _____

10 The volcano was INIVE and no longer spewed out molten lava.   _____

Find the letter which will end the first word and start the second word.

Example   peac (h) ome

11 fin   (___) oze

12 mal   (___) ive

13 poin (___) rip

14 kis   (___) ite

15 me   (___) age

Write the letters of each of the following words in alphabetical order, then circle the fifth letter in each word.

16 FAMILY   _____

17 READING   _____

18 LIGHTER   _____

19 TUESDAY   _____

20 BOUNCE   _____

Find the four-letter word hidden at the end of one word and the beginning of the next word. The order of the letters may not be changed.

Example The children had bats and balls. _sand_

21 Sarah asked her brother to turn his music down. _____

22 The teacher announced that there appeared to be a problem with the computers. _____

23 The corporal ordered his troops to stand to attention. _____

24 'Please stop interrupting!' said the teacher. _____

25 The sofa remained in place by the door. _____   **5**

Add one letter to the word in capital letters to make a new word. The meaning of the new word is given in the clue.

Example PLAN   simple   _plain_

26 EVER   not at all   _____

27 STRIP   a band of colour   _____

28 CHAP   not expensive   _____

29 THOUGH   in one side and out the other   _____

30 RESTED   taken by force   _____   **5**

Complete the following sentences by selecting the most sensible word from each group of words given in the brackets. Underline the words selected.

Example The (<u>children</u>, books, foxes) carried the (houses, <u>books</u>, steps) home from the (greengrocer, <u>library</u>, factory).

31 (Two, three, four) times (three, four, five) makes (eight, eighteen, eighty).

32 The (force, black, strong) wind blew through the (broken, pattern, fast) window.

33 In which (shirt, shop, shape) can we buy (card, painted, chocolate) (clouds, swimmers, cakes)?

34 Who (was, would, wish) like to (eat, hide, try) on their new school (uniform, canteen, hall)?

35 We were (shot, ate, flew) at by an (untidy, uneaten, unseen) (lunch, army, bedroom).   **5**

Complete the following sentences in the best way by choosing one word from each set of brackets.

Example Tall is to (tree, <u>short</u>, colour) as narrow is to (thin, white, <u>wide</u>).

36 Shout is to (whisper, scream, noisy) as loud is to (low, quiet, cosy).

37 Hat is to (face, head, coat) as mittens is to (cat, wool, hands).

38 Government is to (rule, elect, law) as school is to (teach, classroom, pupil).

39 Red is to (food, danger, colour) as centimetre is to (weight, green, measurement).

40 Grand is to (grown, impressive, lesson) as modest is to (reduced, proud, plain).

 5

Fill in the crosswords so that all the given words are included. You have been given one letter as a clue in each crossword.

 B 19

41

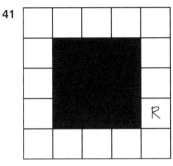

salad, daily, scale, entry

42

water, rings, yards, windy

43

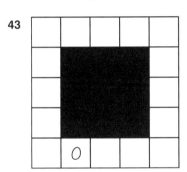

roads, elves, frame, fever

44

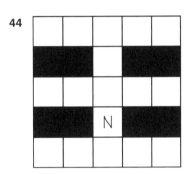

miser, sunny, funny, tryst

45

loves, caves, halls, misty

 5

If the code for TRAVEL is USBWFM, what are the codes for the following words?

B 24

46 LEVEL   ———————

47 LEAVE   ———————

48 EVER   ———————

 3

If the code for CUTE is DVUF, what do these codes stand for?

B 24

49 SBSF _____

50 MJTU _____

2

If $a = 3$, $b = 5$, $c = 12$, $d = 15$, $e = 2$, $f = 10$, give the answers to these calculations as letters.

B 26

51 $d - f =$ _____

52 $a + e =$ _____

53 $b \times a =$ _____

54 $d \div a =$ _____

55 $b \times e =$ _____

5

Choose the word or phrase that makes each sentence true.

B 14

Example   A LIBRARY always has (posters, a carpet, <u>books</u>, DVDs, stairs).

56 A DESK always has (glass, books, pens, legs, children).

57 A LAKE is always (sandy, wet, salty, blue, deep).

58 A TRUCK always has (a roof, four seats, passengers, petrol, carpet).

59 A COUNTRY always has (a king, a queen, a parliament, a border, a president).

60 GLASS is always (hard, transparent, clean, square, frosted).

5

B 25

Peter and Ruth Jones

David Jones and Joan Thomas   Jessica Jones and Mark Stevens

Molly Jones   Olivia Stevens

61 Peter is David's (brother, uncle, father, grandfather).

62 Jessica is Ruth's (sister, aunt, mother, daughter).

63 Molly is Ruth's (daughter, sister, mother, granddaughter).

64 Olivia is David's (daughter, niece, mother, sister).

65 Peter is Mark's (father, brother, grandfather, father-in-law).

5

Paper 6

Underline the pair of words most similar in meaning.

    Example come, go   <u>roams, wanders</u>   fear, fare

1 awake, asleep   gift, present   sweet, bitter

2 top, peak   warm, cool   hole, hill

3 big, small   question, answer   follow, pursue

4 please, delight   create, destroy   fall, rise

5 failure, victory   judgement, decision   allow, refuse

Find the three-letter word which can be added to the letters in capitals to make a new word. The new word will complete the sentence sensibly.

Example   The cat sprang onto the MO. <u>USE</u>

6 He found it difficult to SK as his mouth was so dry.   ———

7 You must MULLY three by three to get 9.   ———

8 SE birthday is it today?   ———

9 She found the question difficult to UNDERSD.   ———

10 The sisters had a DISAGREET over who should get the bed near the window.   ———

Find the letter which will end the first word and start the second word.

    Example peac (<u>h</u>) ome

11 fligh (—) rip

12 pra   (—) onder

13 flak (—) nd

14 ris   (—) ite

15 bea (—) rial

Rearrange the muddled letters in capitals to make a proper word. The answer will complete the sentence sensibly.

    Example A BEZAR is an animal with stripes.   <u>ZEBRA</u>

16 The time is now a ATEQRRU past five.   —————

17 He had VESRREED the car into the parking space.   —————

18 I like to have some RVYAG on my mashed potatoes. _____

19 The manager named the SRELPAY for the next match. _____

20 In the drought, we were all asked to NCVROSEE water. _____

B 21

Find the four-letter word hidden at the end of one word and the beginning of the next word. The order of the letters may not be changed.

    Example   The children had bats and balls.   _sand_

21 The Vikings fled overland before regrouping. _____

22 Many frozen icecaps are found north of Canada. _____

23 Each term my school tests the fire alarm to make sure it is working. _____

24 Kevin ended the conversation fairly quickly. _____

25 Tom's biggest problem was the neighbours playing loud music. _____

B 18

Change the first word of the third pair in the same way as the other pairs to give a new word.

    Example   bind, hind   bare, hare   but, _hut_

26 race, rate   face, fate   place, _____

27 can, cane   trip, tripe   prim, _____

28 port, sort   pane, sane   page, _____

29 stark, shark   stone, shone   stock, _____

30 file, life   pole, lope   ride, _____

B 17

Find and underline the two words which need to change places for each sentence to make sense.

    Example   She went to <u>letter</u> the <u>write</u>.

31 When go you like to would to the zoo?

32 Nature is an amazing wonder of flying.

33 Island is an Britain nation in the continent of Europe.

34 I am planning to deposit fifty bank in the pounds.

35 Gabriel found that the heat about questions were extremely difficult to do.

B 15

Choose two words, one from each set of brackets, to complete the sentences in the best way.

    Example   Tall is to (tree, <u>short</u>, colour) as narrow is to (thin, white, <u>wide</u>).

36 Sugar is to (grain, sweet, bitter) as lemon is to (lime, drink, sour).

37 True is to (argument, lie, truth) as vain is to (calm, preen, vanity).

38 Salad is to (can, fork, vegetables) as trifle is to (eat, pie, fruit).

39 Tooth is to (foot, mouth, clean) as brain is to (skull, nerves, blood).

40 Still is to (calm, active, fizzy) as movement is to (fast, motion, bubbly).

Fill in the crosswords so that all the given words are included. You have been given one letter as a clue in each crossword.

small, revel, tails, taper

trays, place, paint, edges

thick, falls, stick, fount

feeds, bride, taste, ideas

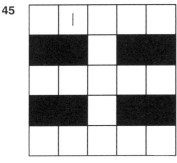

cures, moves, diver, wider

Rearrange the letters in capitals to make another word. The new word has something to do with the first two words or phrases.

	Example	spot	soil	SAINT	<u>STAIN</u>
46	final	end	SALT	_____
47	prickle	bush	NORTH	_____

48	story	yarn	LATE	_____
49	rotten	not fresh	LEAST	_____
50	servant	hard worker	VALES	_____

5

If a = 10, b = 2, c = 3, d = 7, e = 5, give the answers to these calculations as letters.

B 26

51 $b + c + e = $ _____

52 $be = $ _____

53 $a - e = $ _____

54 $(d - b) \times b = $ _____

55 $a \div b = $ _____

5

Change one word so that the sentence makes sense. Underline the word you are taking out and write your new word on the line.

B 14

   Example   I waited in line to buy a <u>book</u> to see the film.   *ticket*

56 The train for Birmingham left the port on time.   _____

57 During the freezing summer months, snow fell almost daily.   _____

58 The teacher examined his patient with a stethoscope.   _____

59 Queen Victoria reigned for many days in the nineteenth century.   _____

60 The florist sold loaves, rolls and a selection of cakes.   _____

5

Rajeev buys three magazines every week. He likes magazines about pop music, computer games and television. Carl hates football, but buys a pop music magazine. Gill buys pop music and fashion magazines. Saskia does not buy any magazines.

B 25

61 Which is the most popular magazine?   _____

62 How many children buy computer game magazines?   _____

2

Jan, Cilla, Vijay and Finn are friends. Finn and Vijay like gymnastics. The other children like hockey. Jan and Finn like tennis. Cilla's favourite is hockey, but she hates gymnastics. All but Finn like swimming.

B 25

63 Which is the most popular sport?   _____

64 Who likes gymnastics and swimming?   _____

65 Who likes three sports?   _____

3

Paper 7

Underline the word in the brackets closest in meaning to the word in capitals.

B 5

Example UNHAPPY (unkind death laughter <u>sad</u> friendly)

1 TRACK (music frame scale path bed)

2 FRAIL (weak lively success timely true)

3 SOFA (table settee television bunk pillow)

4 ANTIQUE (tasty ornament fresh steady old)

5 DOMESTICATED (famous wild tamed hunted criminal)

5

Underline the pair of words most opposite in meaning.

B 9

Example cup, mug   coffee, milk   <u>hot, cold</u>

6 spend, save   dye, colour   fall, drop

7 fly, float   advance, retreat   clue, hint

8 soak, wet   open, full   reckless, careful

9 flexible, rigid   gentle, soft   damp, moist

10 build, support   wind, crank   clutter, order

5

Find the letter which will end the first word and start the second word.

B 10

Example peac (<u>h</u>) ome

11 fla   (—) ongue

12 mirro (—) ain

13 cak   (—) nter

14 ove   (—) ew

15 fur   (—) ield

5

Find a word that can be put in front of each of the following words to make new, compound words.

B 11

Example CAST FALL WARD POUR   <u>DOWN</u>

16 HILL   STAIRS   SET   KEEP   _____

17 FALL   SHIRT   MARE   CLUB   _____

18	MILL	FALL	MELON	PROOF	_____
19	HOUSE	POST	KEEPER	WAY	_____
20	STOP	WAY	FRAME	MAN	_____

B 21

Find the four-letter word hidden at the end of one word and the beginning of the next word. The order of the letters may not be changed.

Example   The children had bats and balls.   _sand_

21 Please replace that book on the shelf later. _____

22 That ornament would be extremely valuable if it were not damaged. _____

23 People of my age are often asked to give advice on living a long life. _____

24 The spies watched the suspects through binoculars. _____

25 It is clear that the sack needed some urgent repair. _____

B 13

Change the first word into the last word, by changing one letter at a time and making a new, different word in the middle.

Example   CASE   _CASH_   LASH

26 FAST   _____   FACE

27 FINE   _____   FARE

28 TRAY   _____   TRIP

29 FLEW   _____   CLAW

30 BEST   _____   BEAR

B 14

Complete the following sentences by selecting the most sensible word from each group of words given in the brackets. Underline the words selected.

Example   The (children, books, foxes) carried the (houses, books, steps) home from the greengrocer, library, factory).

31 The (cow, bird, girl) sat on its (nest, chair, floor), looking after its (chicks, cubs, hands).

32 The (lazy, late, first) man on the (river, moon, sun) wore a special (spacesuit, oar, cane).

33 The (pink, young, brown) leaves fell off the (cat, trees, sky) in (autumn, spring, grass).

34 A (rabbit, friend, doctor) has to (eat, march, train) for many (meals, lungs, years).

35 The fast moving (man, river, beaver) flowed (quickly, hungrily, lazily) to the (sky, race, sea).

Find and underline the two words which need to change places for each sentence to make sense.

Example She went to <u>letter</u> the <u>write</u>.

36 You should never full with your mouth speak.

37 Can't have each we a piece of cake?

38 Health is good for your swimming.

39 It was a very pretty day on the warm beach.

40 The old car got into his battered man.

Complete the following expressions by filling in the missing word.

Example Pen is to ink as brush is to _paint_

41 Box is to lid as house is to _____ .

42 Love is to hate as laugh is to _____ .

43 Tall is to taller as cool is to _____ .

44 Wales is to Welsh as Spain is to _____ .

45 Scarf is to neck as glove is to _____ .

Fill in the crosswords so that all the given words are included. You have been given one letter as a clue in each crossword.

46

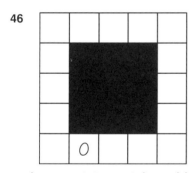

house, state, match, maids

47

fight, flake, tiger, error

48

haunt, right, river, roach

49

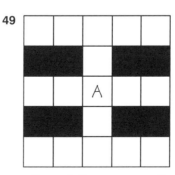

sites, plait, aspen, avail

50

dress, trees, cider, tasty

If a = 2, b = 4, c = 6, d = 8 and e = 12, find the value of the following calculations.

51 e + b = _____

52 e − a = _____

53 a × b = _____

54 (e − d) + c = _____

55 $\dfrac{d}{b}$ = _____

Rearrange the letters in capitals to make another word. The new word has something to do with the first two words.

    Examples spot soil   SAINT <u>STAIN</u>

56 javelin   point   REAPS   _____

57 begin   commence   TARTS   _____

58 tassle   edge   FINGER   _____

59 quiet   hushed   LISTEN   _____

60 support   love   RACE   _____

Choose the word or phrase that makes each sentence true.

Example   A LIBRARY always has (posters, a carpet, <u>books</u>, DVDs, stairs).

61 A SHOP always has (carpets, goods, dresses, women, stairs).

62 A BANK always has (customers, men, pictures, mirrors, money).

63 A PARTY always has (music, food, balloons, guests, gifts).

64 A GARDEN always has (flowers, a bench, trees, earth, a swing).

65 A FLORIST always has (balloons, toys, flowers, chocolates, trees).

Now go to the Progress Chart to record your score!   Total   65

Paper 1

1. test, exam
2. rot, decay
3. eat, consume
4. light, pale
5. extend, enlarge
6. then, now
7. large, tiny
8. loose, tight
9. hollow, solid
10. first, final
11. teacher, children, lunches
12. try, swimming, tide
13. cows, huddled, field
14. team, goal, match
15. whisked, dessert, fork
16. SHADES, DASHES
17. TEARS, RATES
18. PEARS, SPEAR
19. FLESH, SHELF
20. STEAL, LEAST
21. tear
22. carp
23. loan
24. moon
25. calm
26. e
27. t
28. m
29. r
30. p
31. lake, boat
32. you, I
33. mechanic, car
34. is, do
35. caged, angry
36. TU
37. XV
38. NO
39. Z11
40. CE
41. b
42. s
43. m
44. y
45. a
46.

47.

48.

49.

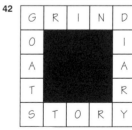

50.

51. * − : &
52. $ − : *
53. & − : £ −
54. TAR
55. TAINT
56. tamed
57. every
58. matted
59. games
60. dimmer
61. groan
62. Fettle
63. Hambury
64. 16 km
65. 1 km

Paper 2

1. build, construct
2. put, place
3. attempt, try
4. grave, serious
5. easy, effortless
6. false, true
7. continuous, ended
8. plain, elegant
9. criticise, praise
10. well, ill
11. flatmate
12. attack
13. forsake
14. outcry
15. invest
16. ROT
17. LOW
18. MAT
19. ONE
20. ATE
21. here
22. rope
23. rare
24. play
25. ease
26. POSH
27. SEAR
28. LOST
29. MINE
30. STAG
31. arrive, holiday, resort
32. way, go, theatre
33. learner, stalling, engine
34. haunted, castle, spirit
35. mathematics, graphs, numbers
36. Thursday, Saturday
37. sailing, ship
38. shore, lake
39. restricted, unlimited
40. considerate, generous
41.

42.

43.

44

I	R	A	T	E
		F		
L	A	T	E	R
		E		
F	O	R	G	E

45

M	O	C	H	A
		H		
P	L	E	A	T
		S		
M	E	T	R	E

46 54
47 21
48 7
49 25
50 16
51 < > ? ? %
52 ? £ % X
53 % X > <
54 ILL
55 CALL
56 drained
57 plank
58 version
59 nearest
60 plain
61 4
62 England
63 Eleanor
64 2 km
65 Jessica and Lianne

Paper 3

1 drag
2 butterfly
3 apple
4 agreement
5 Russia
6 love, hate
7 hard, effortless
8 waste, conserve
9 fair, dark
10 infinite, limited
11 e
12 e
13 l
14 o
15 n
16 DOOR
17 STAND
18 TIME
19 NEWS
20 HEART

21 send
22 seem
23 area
24 cart
25 sage
26 have, could
27 computer, school
28 four, two
29 steal, right
30 China, world
31 3
32 55
33 16
34 23
35 27

36

P	A	I	N	T
R				H
I				E
C				I
E	N	T	E	R

37

S	T	A	N	D
H				R
A				A
D				F
E	V	E	N	T

38

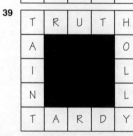

F	L	A	I	R
A				E
I				I
N				G
T	H	O	R	N

39

T	R	U	T	H
A				O
I				L
N				L
T	A	R	D	Y

40

M	A	G	I	C
		H		
F	L	O	W	N
		S		
A	T	T	I	C

41 aged, young
42 shoe, leather
43 lessen, multiply
44 change, remain
45 unique, original
46 ' £ $ %
47 £ & * ^
48 BALL
49 BEAN
50 ACHE
51 relay
52 alert
53 rested
54 starve
55 ignore
56 James
57 Soraya, Lena
58 Kim
59 4
60 2
61 WALK
62 FINAL
63 LESSON
64 SPENT
65 LETTERS

Paper 4

1 push, shove
2 weep, cry
3 mend, repair
4 control, manage
5 uphold, support
6 DIN
7 HAM
8 ARM
9 INK
10 MAN
11 k
12 e
13 y
14 m
15 e
16 OUT
17 IRON
18 SNOW
19 EYE
20 POST
21 chin
22 meal
23 idea
24 dead
25 heap
26 but
27 rice
28 steer
29 fare
30 leap
31 girl, school, first
32 taking, test, week
33 climbing, dangerous, weather
34 wondered, try, assistance

35 never, brush, teeth
36 woman, time
37 been, have
38 the, all
39 tell, time
40 that, why
41 ninth
42 French
43 century
44 down
45 wet
46 O, R
47 DG, DH
48 D9, F13
49 UF, OL
50 ZY, VU
51 LGAC
52 TWIG
53 MQRO
54 ZDLW
55 HSK
56 cola
57 Siobhan
58 Bangor
59 5
60 27
61 32
62 5 years
63 4
64 2
65 8

Paper 5

1–5 Give one mark for each two correct answers: skipping G, basket C, Cluedo G, urn C, den H, flat H, cup C, lodge H, casket C, snakes and ladders G.

6 ROT
7 MEN
8 ASH
9 PEN
10 ACT
11 d
12 l
13 t
14 s
15 w
16 Ⓜ
17 Ⓘ
18 Ⓛ
19 Ⓣ
20 Ⓞ
21 herb
22 reap
23 lord
24 pint
25 fare
26 never
27 stripe
28 cheap
29 through

30 wrested
31 two, four, eight
32 strong, broken
33 shop, chocolate, cakes
34 would, try, uniform
35 shot, unseen, army
36 whisper, quiet
37 head, hands
38 rule, teach
39 colour, measurement
40 impressive, plain

41

42

43

44

45

46 MFWFM
47 MFBWF
48 FWFS

49 RARE
50 LIST
51 b
52 b
53 d
54 b
55 f
56 legs
57 wet
58 a roof
59 a border
60 hard
61 father
62 daughter
63 granddaughter
64 niece
65 father-in-law

Paper 6

1 gift, present
2 top, peak
3 follow, pursue
4 please, delight
5 judgement, decision
6 PEA
7 TIP
8 WHO
9 TAN
10 MEN
11 t
12 y
13 e
14 k
15 t
16 QUARTER
17 REVERSED
18 GRAVY
19 PLAYERS
20 CONSERVE
21 dove
22 nice
23 real
24 vine
25 then
26 plate
27 prime
28 sage
29 shock
30 dire
31 go, would
32 Nature, flying
33 Island, Britain
34 bank, pounds
35 heat, questions
36 sweet, sour
37 truth, vanity
38 vegetables, fruit
39 mouth, skull
40 calm, motion

41

42

43

44

45

46 LAST
47 THORN
48 TALE
49 STALE
50 SLAVE
51 a
52 a
53 e
54 a
55 e
56 port, station
57 summer, winter
58 teacher, doctor
59 days, years
60 florist, baker
61 pop music
62 1
63 swimming
64 Vijay
65 Jan

Paper 7

1 path
2 weak
3 settee
4 old
5 tamed
6 spend, save
7 advance, retreat
8 reckless, careful
9 flexible, rigid
10 clutter, order
11 t
12 r
13 e
14 n
15 y
16 UP
17 NIGHT
18 WATER
19 GATE
20 DOOR
21 flat
22 torn
23 gear
24 swat
25 knee
26 FACT
27 FIRE
28 TRAP
29 FLAW
30 BEAT
31 bird, nest, chicks
32 first, moon, spacesuit
33 brown, trees, autumn
34 doctor, train, years
35 river, quickly, sea
36 full, speak
37 have, we
38 health, swimming
39 pretty, warm
40 car, man
41 roof
42 cry
43 cooler
44 Spanish
45 hand

46

47

48

49

50

51 16
52 10
53 8
54 10
55 2
56 SPEAR
57 START
58 FRINGE
59 SILENT
60 CARE
61 goods
62 money
63 guests

A4

64 earth
65 flowers

Paper 8

1–5 *Give one mark for each two correct answers:* noun B, monitor C, verb B, violin A, disk drive C, mouse C, guitar A, preposition B, piano A, flute A.

6 pull, push
7 wild, tame
8 shut, open
9 combine, separate
10 friend, enemy
11 s
12 y
13 l
14 t
15 l
16 takeaway
17 update
18 blameless
19 office
20 peanut
21 wasp
22 bush
23 thin
24 seat
25 army
26 RICE
27 MEAT
28 PLAY
29 FLAT
30 BEAR
31 O15
32 YW
33 FI
34 PD
35 MO

36
T	R	U	S	T
A				H
M				O
E				S
S	H	O	V	E

37
P	R	I	Z	E
R				V
E				E
S				R
S	U	N	N	Y

38
I	C	I	N	G
N				R
P				A
U				V
T	A	N	G	Y

39
U	L	T	R	A
	Y			
H	A	P	P	Y
	E			
H	A	S	T	Y

40
F	U	N	N	Y
	I			
R	I	G	H	T
	H			
T	I	T	L	E

41 sort
42 play
43 fly
44 stab
45 kid
46 TIE
47 MAT
48 RED
49 LEAP
50 TALE
51 blue team
52 15
53 10
54 Tuesday
55 14
56 e
57 b
58 c
59 f
60 b
61 EGILMNT
62 T
63 G
64 ARSTY
65 S

Paper 9

1 bread
2 right
3 bold
4 scream
5 amazed
6 sad

7 raise
8 arrive
9 exclude
10 join
11 RUM
12 RAN
13 OWN
14 ARM
15 TEA
16 undertake
17 upright
18 throughout
19 downstairs
20 cupboard
21 then
22 bite
23 send
24 pout
25 mask
26 fit, flame
27 word, tolls
28 mile, self
29 able, scarf
30 rob, event
31 goalkeeper, save, match
32 eat, vegetables, good
33 old, walk, stick
34 dress, modern, belt
35 time, ancient, witch
36 huge, short
37 early, excited
38 crowded, bare
39 fasten, twist
40 rest, stay

41
Q	U	I	L	L
U				A
E				R
E				G
R	A	N	G	E

42
F	L	O	O	R
R				H
I				Y
E				M
D	R	A	P	E

43
C	R	E	P	E
H				R
E				A
E				S
R	I	F	L	E

44

G	R	A	V	E
		F		
M	I	T	R	E
		E		
F	I	R	E	S

45

B	I	T	E	S
		R		
T	H	A	N	K
		P		
T	A	S	T	E

46 PK, PM
47 M, S
48 Q9, O11
49 OJ, RH
50 KM, PH
51 7325
52 5237
53 5247
54 1352
55 1852
56 ACJKOPST
57 T
58 K
59 CNORTUY
60 T
61 Jem
62 10
63 English
64 German
65 Italian

Paper 10

1 sponge, ship
2 twig, nest
3 heart, friend
4 next, future
5 undecided, complicated
6 INK
7 TEN
8 PAR
9 LIT
10 OUR
11 rot
12 dice
13 deal
14 bear
15 treat
16 bare

17 torn
18 fear
19 hall
20 arch
21 late, cramp
22 prim, gape
23 tile, sight
24 stand, brought
25 mine, clay
26 lunch
27 sly
28 knock
29 poke
30 green
31 horse, hay, stable
32 night, hooting, distance
33 road, ways, traffic
34 teacher, pupils, homework
35 girls, mother, cinema
36 outside, rainy
37 year, day
38 month, first
39 lunch, lasagne
40 mother, baby
41 LN
42 S19
43 OP
44 WU
45 TV
46 quick, slow
47 save, spend
48 attack, retreat
49 near, distant
50 specific, general
51–55 citsilaer, taerter, tcane, tcarter, tsomla
56 612
57 9123
58 9136
59 SURE
60 HUES
61 toffee and fudge
62 chocolate and sweets
63 Eric
64 Ann
65 Farook

Paper 11

1 cheerful, happy
2 disappear, vanish
3 flash, flare
4 career, profession
5 pay, salary
6 ROW
7 RAW
8 KIN
9 SIT

10 TAR
11 HOUSE
12 SEA
13 DOWN
14 BACK
15 WATCH
16 hate
17 ants
18 sour
19 slay
20 rope
21 GALE
22 POST OR PART
23 BEST
24 CREW
25 SPAR
26 radio, music
27 reach, managed
28 month, day
29 hunting, lions
30 queue, wait

31

S	T	U	N	T
L				H
E				E
E				S
P	L	A	C	E

32

F	E	E	L	S
R				L
O				A
W				Y
N	A	M	E	S

33

C	H	O	S	E
H				N
I				D
E				E
F	R	E	E	D

34

S	E	V	E	N
		E		
P	R	I	S	M
		L		
H	A	S	T	E

A6

35

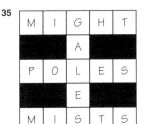

M	I	G	H	T
		A		
P	O	L	E	S
		E		
M	I	S	T	S

- 36 AK, AM
- 37 OS, RV
- 38 LI, NK
- 39 DQ, DO
- 40 IR, HS
- 41 ♦ ○ • ♥
- 42 & ♥ ♦ ○ •
- 43 ○ • ♥ ♦ ▲
- 44 HEAR
- 45 RATE
- 46–47 Eagles eat mice. Eagles are predators
- 48–49 Spain is hot. Palm trees never grow in cold countries.
- 50–51 Earth is further from the Sun than Venus. Venus is hotter than Earth.
- 52 *Eastenders*
- 53 Joaquin
- 54 Molly
- 55 Rashid and Tom
- 56 t
- 57 q
- 58 s
- 59 r
- 60 u
- 61 PCKN
- 62 QDRS
- 63 GOOD
- 64 BSX
- 65 QLRDE

Paper 12

- 1 smart, fast
- 2 body, smile
- 3 mud, sand
- 4 desert, ocean
- 5 field, meadow
- 6 PEN
- 7 PIP
- 8 ADD
- 9 EAR
- 10 APE
- 11 y
- 12 r
- 13 t
- 14 r
- 15 l
- 16 netball
- 17 flatmate
- 18 pattern

- 19 goodwill
- 20 manage
- 21 hiss
- 22 mane
- 23 pear
- 24 tilt
- 25 vein
- 26 self, shell
- 27 brow, shone
- 28 hare, smash
- 29 rate, pact
- 30 last, tone
- 31 trees, leaves
- 32 race, first
- 33 bowl, breakfast
- 34 silver, gold
- 35 find, dig
- 36 HX
- 37 QN
- 38 WM
- 39 WD
- 40 JQ
- 41 3491
- 42 3428
- 43 3528
- 44 2849
- 45 2528
- 46 Li
- 47 cat and dog
- 48 Sharif
- 49 2
- 50 5
- 51 h
- 52 h
- 53 f
- 54 d
- 55 h
- 56 <u>flower</u>, petrol
- 57 <u>garage</u>, vet
- 58 <u>moon's</u>, sun's
- 59 <u>foot</u>, neck
- 60 <u>marshmallow</u>, cream
- 61 UDWHV
- 62 RNWO
- 63 SALE
- 64 SHOW
- 65 PDVN

Paper 13

- 1 B
- 2 D
- 3 C
- 4 A
- 5 B
- 6 hunt, search
- 7 similar, alike
- 8 overtake, pass
- 9 show, display
- 10 vague, unclear
- 11 pass
- 12 conflict

- 13 damage
- 14 follow
- 15 doubtful
- 16 can
- 17 light
- 18 hit
- 19 bright
- 20 smart
- 21 GREEN
- 22 WOOD
- 23 FIRE
- 24 HAND
- 25 HAIR
- 26 sand
- 27 lace
- 28 torn
- 29 term
- 30 fort
- 31 man
- 32 sore
- 33 plot
- 34 hop
- 35 rip
- 36 bake, oven
- 37 Bindy, Annabel
- 38 homework, fingers
- 39 red, wild
- 40 red, read
- 41 e
- 42 h
- 43 r
- 44 t
- 45 k
- 46 3115
- 47 8277
- 48 2751
- 49 5117
- 50 3297
- 51 David
- 52 Peter
- 53 16
- 54 23
- 55 Town D
- 56 PAIRS
- 57 EXITS
- 58 SAUCE
- 59 SAGE
- 60 DANGER
- 61 <u>butcher</u>, baker
- 62 <u>tame</u>, wild
- 63 <u>hole</u>, nest
- 64 <u>Sunday</u>, December
- 65 <u>nurse</u>, teacher

Paper 14

- 1 swift, fast
- 2 back, rear
- 3 miniature, small
- 4 aim, goal
- 5 pole, rod

6 brilliant, dull
7 rude, polite
8 rise, fall
9 criticise, praise
10 relaxed, tense
11 plain
12 grace
13 pack
14 grain
15 star
16 e
17 t
18 d
19 k
20 p
21 hole
22 edge
23 cane
24 this
25 rind
26 PART
27 MIST
28 SOAR
29 BRAT
30 CUTS
31 TEST
32 ALSO
33 PEAR
34 PINT
35 RARE
36 r
37 e
38 t
39 t
40 b
41 pound, beat
42 lower, reduce
43 injure, damage
44 sickness, illness
45 tough, strong
46 WAR
47 WATER
48 WEATHER

49 PASS
50 BACK
51 QN, UN
52 CC, XX
53 RP, PN
54 PO, PQ
55 I5, K6
56 PEAR
57 CLAP
58 PALE
59 LEER
60 PALACE
61 wake, sleep
62 notes, strings
63 alive, dead
64 moon, sun
65 hungry, full

Paper 15

1 ask, request
2 shiny, glistening
3 destroyed, broken
4 cross, angry
5 drum, tap
6 shy, confident
7 cause, effect
8 light, heavy
9 tired, energetic
10 rare, common
11 r
12 b
13 l
14 r
15 y
16 lone
17 shun
18 cast
19 itch
20 heat
21 b
22 c

23 t
24 f
25 w
26 dragon
27 cove
28 ration
29 shin
30 meter
31 track, train
32 England, Kent
33 films, music
34 home, late
35 house, newspaper
36 slow, high
37 overlook, honour
38 water, coal
39 wet, cold
40 bird, mammal
41 10
42 45
43 E
44 E
45 D
46 m
47 y
48 e
49 d
50 l
51 LEAP
52 FALSE
53 WEAK
54 ANGERS
55 MELON
56 PAST
57 MACE or MITE
58 ARMS
59 SNIP
60 FLAW
61 EO
62 WW
63 ST
64 ZV
65 Z26

Paper 8

Look at these groups of words.

A	B	C
Musical instruments	Parts of speech	Computer terms

1–5 Choose the correct group for each of the words below. Write in the letter.

noun ___   monitor ___   verb ___   violin ___   disk drive ___

mouse ___   guitar ___   preposition ___   piano ___   flute ___

Underline the pair of words most opposite in meaning.

Example   cup, mug   coffee, milk   <u>hot, cold</u>

6 start, begin   pull, push   fight, battle

7 wild, tame   medium, middle   stale, old

8 shut, open   tight, cramped   fix, mend

9 try, attempt   combine, separate   stay, remain

10 filter, flow   friend, enemy   bump, knock

Find the letter that will end the first word and start the second word.

Example   peac (<u>h</u>) ome

11 dres (___) ign

12 pla (___) oke

13 shal (___) ove

14 trai (___) iara

15 dril (___) ong

Underline the two words, one from each group, that go together to form a new word. The word in the first group always comes first.

Example   (hand, <u>green</u>, for)   (light, <u>house</u>, sure)

16 (take, bring, seat)   (home, away, back)

17 (up, in, at)   (day, week, date)

18 (hunt, weak, blame)   (on, less, full)

19 (on, off, down)   (rest, step, ice)

20 (snap, pea, spice)   (nut, bag, hot)

Find the four-letter word hidden at the end of one word and the beginning of the next word. The order of the letters may not be changed.

Example   The children had bats and balls.   <u>sand</u>

21 Joe was pleased he didn't have any homework that night.   _____

22 We were surprised when the bus halted at the stop.   _____

23 Mark felt proud of himself for finishing fourth in the race.   _____

24 Apples eaten quickly will give you indigestion.   _____

25 The car my brother just bought is bright red.   _____

Change the first word into the last word, by changing one letter at a time and making a new, different word in the middle.

Example   CASE   <u>CASH</u>   LASH

26 NICE   _____   RACE

27 SEAT   _____   MOAT

28 PLAN   _____   SLAY

29 FEAT   _____   FLAY

30 BEAN   _____   TEAR

Fill in the missing letters and numbers. The alphabet has been written out to help you.

A B C D E F G H I J K L M N O P Q R S T U V W X Y Z

Example   AB is to CD as PQ is to <u>RS</u>

31 C3 is to E5 as M13 is to   _____

32 WU is to TR as BZ is to   _____

33 HK is to MP as AD is to   _____

34 RR is to XL as JJ is to   _____

35 AC is to EG as IK is to   _____

Fill in the crosswords so that all the given words are included. You have been given one letter as a clue in each crossword.

36

those, trust, tames, shove

37

press, prize, every, sunny

38

gravy, input, tangy, icing

39

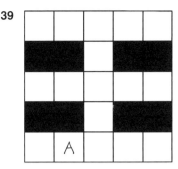

types, ultra, hasty, happy

40

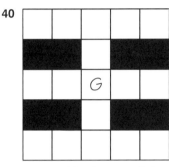

right, title, funny, night

Underline the one word in brackets which will go equally well with both pairs of words outside the brackets.

Example   rush, attack   cost, fee   (price, hasten, strike, <u>charge</u>, money)

41 kind, type   select, choose   (sort, gentle, take, pass, soft)

42 frolic, romp   performance, drama   (joy, act, jump, play, game)

43 insect, bug   travel, aeroplane   (fly, ant, hear, floor, listen)

44 attempt, try   knife, jab   (go, sword, stab, stake, point)

45 child, young   tease, fool   (kid, trick, badger, fox, tail)

46 If 7345 stands for TIME, 735 stands for   _____.

47 If 2839 stands for TAME, 382 stands for   _____.

48 If 4337 stands for DEER, 734 stands for   _____.

49 If 6913 stands for PEAL, 3916 stands for   _____.

50 If 4321 stands for LATE, 2341 stands for   _____.

In a class athletics competition, the blue team scored 20 points. The yellow team got five points more than the red team. The green team scored eight points less than the highest of these teams. The red team scored half as many points as the blue team.

B 25

51 Which team came top? _____

52 How many points did the yellow team score? _____

53 How many points did the red team score? _____

54 If it was Tuesday two days ago, what day will it be in five days' time? _____

55 If David will be 23 in four years' time, how old was he five years ago? _____

5

If a = 2, b = 4, c = 8, d = 6, e = 10 and f = 12, give the answers to these calculations as letters.

B 26

56 a + c = ___

57 f − c = ___

58 a × b = ___

59 a + b + d = ___

60 c ÷ a = ___

5

Answer these questions. The alphabet has been written out to help you.

B 20

A B C D E F G H I J K L M N O P Q R S T U V W X Y Z

61 Put the letters in MELTING in alphabetical order. _____

62 Which is now the last letter? _____

63 Which is now the second letter? _____

64 Put the letters in TRAYS in alphabetical order. _____

65 Which is now the third letter? _____

5

Now go to the Progress Chart to record your score!   Total   65

Paper 9

Find a word that is similar in meaning to the word in capital letters and that rhymes with the second word.

B 5

Example CABLE   tyre   *wire*

1 LOAF   head   _____

2 CORRECT   flight   _____

3	BRAVE	hold	_____
4	SHOUT	dream	_____
5	SURPRISED	glazed	_____

5

Underline the one word in the brackets which is most opposite in meaning to the word in capitals.

B 6

Example WIDE (broad vague long <u>narrow</u> motorway)

6 JOYFUL (old rich cheerful sad rested)

7 LOWER (drop raise down deep below)

8 LEAVE (behind right arrive go exit)

9 INCLUDE (accept exclude add remain contain)

10 SEPARATE (shrink reduce divide apart join)

5

Find the three-letter word which can be added to the letters in capitals to make a new word. The new word will complete the sentence sensibly.

B 22

Example The cat sprang onto the MO. <u>USE</u>

11 The musicians enjoyed playing their TPETS loudly. _____

12 The food was very good at the Italian RESTAUT. _____

13 The museum contained many royal CRS and robes. _____

14 The choir was singing in perfect HONY. _____

15 The swimming CHER asked the students to dive into the pool. _____

5

Underline two words, one from each group, that go together to form a new word. The word in the first group always comes first.

B 8

Example (hand, <u>green</u>, for) (light, <u>house</u>, sure)

16 (under, side, on) (take, put, out)

17 (to, where, up) (good, right, may)

18 (at, through, in) (out, last, fire)

19 (side, down, on) (stairs, case, ladder)

20 (glass, drink, cup) (board, set, light)

5

Find the four-letter word hidden at the end of one word and the beginning of the next word. The order of the letters may not be changed.

B 21

Example The children had bats and balls. <u>sand</u>

21 We will be the next group to get a table. _____

22 Kate's rabbit enjoys munching on lettuce and carrots. _____

23 Our holiday to Mauritius ended on a Saturday. _____

24 It is difficult to skip outside in the long grass. _____

25 My mum asked everyone to be quiet because the baby was sleeping. _____ ◯ 5

Move one letter from the first word and add it to the second word to make two new words. B 13

    Example   hunt   sip   _hut_   _snip_

26 flit   fame   _____   _____

27 sword   toll   _____   _____

28 smile   elf   _____   _____

29 fable   scar   _____   _____

30 robe   vent   _____   _____   ◯ 5

Complete the following sentences by selecting the most sensible word from each group of words given in the brackets. Underline the words selected. B 14

    Example   The (<u>children</u>, books, foxes) carried the (houses, <u>books</u>, steps) home from the (greengrocer, <u>library</u>, factory).

31 The (score, goalkeeper, spectator) made a wonderful (save, fall, trick) to make sure we won the (treat, match, race).

32 (Eat, wash, dry) up your (water, vegetables, shoes) because they are (late, old, good) for you.

33 He was very (late, hungry, old) and found it hard to (dive, eat, walk) without a (dish, stick, paper).

34 Her (foot, dress, head) was very (modern, flat, wet) and had a wide (belt, eye, pot) on it.

35 Once upon a (day, year, time) in an (empty, ancient, easy) cottage there lived an old (witch, apple, child). ◯ 5

Choose two words, one from each set of brackets, to complete the sentences in the best way. B 15

    Example   Tall is to (tree, <u>short</u>, colour) as narrow is to (thin, white, <u>wide</u>).

36 Tiny is to (wild, small, huge) as long is to (last, little, short).

37 Late is to (first, early, behind) as calm is to (excited, easy, afraid).

38 Full is to (none, crowded, alone) as empty is to (bare, last, food).

39 Tie is to (shirt, bump, fasten) as turn is to (twist, knob, first).

40 Pause is to (continue, rest, worry) as remain is to (stay, important, leftover). ◯ 5

Fill in the crosswords so that all the given words are included. You have been given one letter as a clue in each crossword.

41

large, queer, range, quill

42

rhyme, drape, fried, floor

43

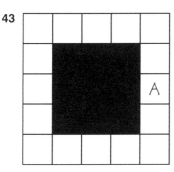

cheer, rifle, crepe, erase

44

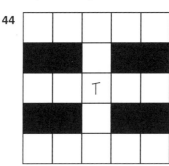

fires, after, mitre, grave

45

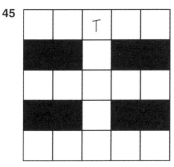

thank, bites, taste, traps

Give the missing letters and numbers in the following sequences. The alphabet has been written out to help you.

A B C D E F G H I J K L M N O P Q R S T U V W X Y Z

	Example	CQ	DQ	EP	FP	_GO_	_HO_
46	PC	PE	PG	PI	___	___
47	D	G	J	___	P	___
48	Y1	W3	U5	S7	___	___
49	CR	FP	IN	LL	___	___
50	AW	BV	DT	GQ	___	___

Here are the number codes for five words. Match the right word to the right code.

PAST	STAR	RATS	STIR	POST
5237	7325	1352	1852	5247

51 RATS _____

52 STAR _____

53 STIR _____

54 PAST _____

55 POST _____

5

56 Arrange the letters in JACKPOTS in alphabetical order. _____

57 Which is now the last letter? _____

58 Which is now the fourth letter? _____

59 Arrange the letters in COUNTRY in alphabetical order. _____

60 Which is now the fifth letter? _____

5

Three little cats are called Jim, Jam and Jem. Jim is three years younger than Jam, but is two years older than Jem, who is five.

61 Who is the youngest? _____

62 How old is Jam? _____

2

Jean, Malek, Geeta, Martin and Sophie are students. Jean and Geeta speak English, German and Spanish. Sophie speaks Italian and German. Martin and Malek speak German, Italian and Spanish.

63 Which language is spoken by the fewest children? _____

64 Which language is spoken by the most children? _____

65 Which language is spoken by three children? _____

3

Now go to the Progress Chart to record your score! Total **65**

Paper 10

Underline the two words which are the odd ones out in the following groups of words.

Example   black   <u>king</u>   purple   green   <u>house</u>

1 sponge   lake   ship   sea   ocean

2 crow   pigeon   twig   nest   eagle

3 love   heart   adore   friend   admire

4 next   aged   future   elderly   old

5 undecided   complicated   conclusion   termination   end

5

Find the three-letter word which can be added to the letters in capitals to make a new word. The new word will complete the sentence sensibly.

Example   The cat sprang onto the MO.   <u>USE</u>

6 Please DR up your juice.   _____

7 The meal lay half EA on the table.   _____

8 I think that you should COME the two options.   _____

9 Being POE is just good manners.   _____

10 I went to the paint shop with my Dad to decide which
   COL I wanted to paint my room.   _____

5

Underline the one word which **can be made** from the letters of the word in capital letters.

Example   CHAMPION   camping   notch   peach   cramp   <u>chimp</u>

11 CONTROL   rot   cannot   call   roll   room

12 DECISION   slide   diesel   noisy   dice   scent

13 SLANDEROUS   gland   race   deal   slate   ended

14 INTOLERABLE   stale   strain   stable   bear   blame

15 ALLITERATION creation   terrain   alight   terrapin   treat

5

Find the four-letter word hidden at the end of one word and the beginning of the next word. The order of the letters may not be changed.

Example   The children had bats and balls.   <u>sand</u>

16 Mum replied that Jake and Caleb aren't playing today.   _____

17 The zoo's alligator never came out of the pool except for food.   _____

18 In those days a serf earned his living with great difficulty. _____

19 It is important to catch all shots coming in his direction. _____

20 The star changed shape when looked at through the telescope. _____

5

Move one letter from the first word and add it to the second word to make two new words.

B 13

Example   hunt   sip   <u>hut</u>   <u>snip</u>

21 plate   cram   _____   _____

22 prime   gap   _____   _____

23 title   sigh   _____   _____

24 strand   bought   _____   _____

25 mince   lay   _____   _____

5

Find a word that is similar in meaning to the word in capital letters and that rhymes with the second word.

B 5

Example   CABLE   tyre   <u>wire</u>

26 MEAL   crunch   _____

27 CRAFTY   fly   _____

28 STRIKE   clock   _____

29 JAB   croak   _____

30 COLOUR   bean   _____

5

Complete the following sentences by selecting the most sensible word from each group of words given in the brackets. Underline the words selected.

B 14

Example   The (<u>children</u>, books, foxes) carried the (houses, <u>books</u>, steps) home from the (greengrocer, <u>library</u>, factory).

31 The (girl, ship, horse) was eating (water, hay, cable) in its (stable, current, bathroom).

32 Later that (week, day, night) an owl was heard (laughing, hooting, walking) in the (distance, flowers, table).

33 Before crossing the (river, road, sky) please look both (rafts, ways, eyes) and listen for (music, traffic, clouds).

34 The (manager, major, teacher) asked his (horses, customers, pupils) to hand in their (homework, teas, umbrellas).

35 The (girls, waiters, dentists) stood in line while their (mayor, mother, mechanic) bought tickets to the (cinema, wedding, party).

5

38

Find and underline the two words which need to change places for each sentence to make sense.

B 17

Example   She went to <u>letter</u> the <u>write</u>.

36 It was too outside to play rainy.

37 The last year of the day is a Sunday.

38 January is the month first of the year.

39 Did you have lunch for your lasagne?

40 The mother was crying until her baby gave her a dummy.

5

Fill in the missing letters and numbers. The alphabet has been written out to help you.

B 23

A B C D E F G H I J K L M N O P Q R S T U V W X Y Z

Example   AB is to CD as PQ is to RS

41 TV is to SU as MO is to _____

42 F6 is to H8 as Q17 is to _____

43 AB is to EF as KL is to _____

44 AC is to ZX as DF is to _____

45 HJ is to QS as KM is to _____

5

Underline the two words, one from each group, which are the most opposite in meaning.

B 9

Example   (dawn, <u>early</u>, wake) (<u>late</u>, stop, sunrise)

46 (quick, lazy, late)   (fast, slow, busy)

47 (change, hunt, save)   (spend, follow, lie)

48 (attempt, attack, attend) (hold, try, retreat)

49 (far, near, away)   (distant, right, move)

50 (single, different, specific) (alone, general, unusual)

5

51–55 Write each word backwards and list them in alphabetical order.

B 20

retract   retreat   almost   enact   realistic

_____   _____   _____   _____   _____

5

If the code for STILE is 36192, what are the codes for the following words?

B 24

56 TIE   _____

57 LIES   _____

58 LIST   _____

3

If the code for RUSHES is 345725, what do the following codes stand for?

B 24

59 5432 _____

60 7425 _____

2

Ann likes sweets and toffee but not chocolate. Her sister, Jean, loves chocolate and fudge. Her friend Beata also likes chocolate and sweets, but hates fudge. Her sister Gosia likes chocolate and sweets.

B 25

61 Which two items are least popular? _____

62 Which two items are most popular? _____

2

Six children are lining up for the cinema. Mohammad is at the front and Ann is third in line. Eric does not stand next to Mohammad or Farook. Charlotte stands between Bob and Eric. Bob and Farook are not at the back of the line.

B 25

63 Who is last in line? _____

64 Who is between Farook and Bob? _____

65 Who is second in line? _____

3

Now go to the Progress Chart to record your score!   Total

65

Paper 11

Underline the two words in each line which are most similar in type or meaning.

B 5

Example <u>dear</u>   pleasant   poor   extravagant   <u>expensive</u>

1 hungry   cheerful   sad   happy   wasteful

2 display   disappear   vanish   wonder   follow

3 flash   thunder   flare   burn   fall

4 sleep   eat   career   make   profession

5 pay   loss   deposit   consideration   salary

5

Find the three-letter word which can be added to the letters in capitals to make a new word. The new word will complete the sentence sensibly.

B 22

Example   The cat sprang onto the MO.   <u>USE</u>

6 The lane was too NAR for a car.   _____

7 My favourite fruit is STBERRIES.   _____

8 A two-piece bathing suit is called a BII.   _____

9 Do not HEATE to call if you need further advice.   _____

10 I prefer NECINES to peaches.   _____

5

Find a word that can be put in front of each of the following words to make a new, compound word.

B 11

Example   CAST   FALL   WARD   POUR   <u>DOWN</u>

11 WORK   BOAT   KEEPER   HOLD   _____

12 SHELL   SHORE   SIDE   SICK   _____

13 STAIRS   POUR   HILL   BEAT   _____

14 STAGE   BONE   FIRE   STROKE   _____

15 TOWER   DOG   WORD   MAKER   _____

5

Find the four-letter word hidden at the end of one word and the beginning of the next word. The order of the letters may not be changed.

B 21

Example   The children had bats and balls.   <u>sand</u>

16 She somehow managed to lose her hat every week.   _____

17 The baby elephant sat down rather clumsily.   _____

18 We made the decorations ourselves.   _____

19 The tiny kittens lay peacefully on the rug.   _____

20 My dad complained because I left the fridge door open.   _____

5

Change the first word into the last word, by changing one letter at a time and making a new, different word in the middle.

B 11

Example   CASE   <u>CASH</u>   LASH

21 GALA   _____   GATE

22 PAST   _____   PORT

23 NEST   _____   BENT

24 CHEW   _____   BREW

25 STAR   _____   SPAT

5

Find and underline the two words which need to change places for each sentence to make sense.

Example   She went to <u>letter</u> the <u>write</u>.

26 The radio on the music was very relaxing.

27 We finally reach to managed the bus stop.

28 His birthday was on the last month of the day.

29 The old hunting were too tired to go lions.

30 Why are we having to queue in this long wait?

5

Fill in the crosswords so that all the given words are included. You have been given one letter as a clue in each crossword.

31
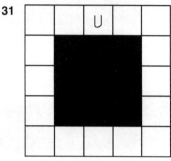

place, sleep, stunt, these

32
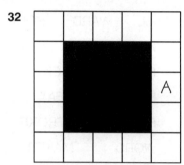

frown, names, slays, feels

33
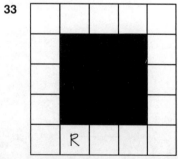

ended, freed, chose, chief

34

seven, prism, haste, veils

35

might, mists, poles, gales

5

Give the two missing pairs of letters in the following sequences. The alphabet has been written out to help you.

B 23

A B C D E F G H I J K L M N O P Q R S T U V W X Y Z

Example   CQ   DQ   EP   FP   *GO*   *HO*

36 AC   AE   AG   AI   _____   _____

37 CG   FJ   IM   LP   _____   _____

38 DA   FC   HE   JG   _____   _____

39 BY   BW   CU   CS   _____   _____

40 MN   LO   KP   JQ   _____   _____

5

If the code for T E A C H E R is ▲ ♥ ♦ ○ ● ♥ &. What are the codes for the following words?

B 24

41 ACHE   _____

42 REACH   _____

43 CHEAT   _____

What do these codes stand for?

44 ● ♥ ♦ &   _____

45 & ♦ ▲ ♥   _____

5

46–47 Read the first statement and then underline two of the five options below that must be true.

B 25

'Eagles hunt small creatures for food.'

Eagles are wild.

Eagles eat mice.

Eagles cannot see well.

People hate eagles.

Eagles are predators.

2

48–49 Read the first two statements and then underline two of the five options below that must be true.

B 25

Palm trees only grow in hot countries. Palm trees are grown in Spain.

Spain is hot.

Palm trees are found in Ireland.

Palm trees never grow in cold countries.

Spain is a city.

Palm trees grow in Antarctica.

2

50–51 Read the first two statements and then underline two of the five options below that must be true.

'Mercury and Venus are planets. They are closer to the Sun than Earth.'

Earth is hotter than Mars.

Earth is further from the Sun than Venus.

Mars is hotter than Venus.

Mercury and Earth are next to each other.

Venus is hotter than Earth.

2

Ewan, Joaquin, Alice and Gemma were discussing their favourite soap operas. Ewan and Alice are the only ones who like *Coronation Street*. Only Gemma and Alice like *Emmerdale*. Joaquin, Ewan and Gemma like *Eastenders*.

B 25

52 Which is the most popular programme? _____

53 Who likes the fewest programmes? _____

2

Rashid, Peta, Molly, Annie and Tom were discussing whether they have a computer, a television or a stereo in their bedroom. Only Peta and Annie did not have a computer. Peta only had a television. Only Rashid and Tom did not have a television. Four children had a stereo.

B 25

54 Who had a computer and television? _____

55 Who had all the same items? _____

2

If p = 2, q = 4, r = 6, s = 8, t = 10 and u = 12, give the answer to these calculations as letters.

B 26

56 q + r = _____

57 u − s = _____

58 p × q = _____

59 u ÷ p = _____

60 p × (u − r) = _____

5

Solve the problems by working out the letter codes. The alphabet has been written out to help you.

B 24

A B C D E F G H I J K L M N O P Q R S T U V W X Y Z

61 In a code, FINAL is written as HKPCN. What is the code for NAIL? _____

62 In a code, BROWN is written as AQNVM. How would you write REST? _____

63 In a code, MILK is written as NJML. What does HPPE stand for? _____

64 In a code, BACK is written as ABBL. How would you write CRY? _____

65 In a code, PRESS is written as MOBPP. How would you write TOUGH? _____

5

Now go to the Progress Chart to record your score!   Total   **65**

Paper 12

Underline the two words which are the odd ones out in the following groups of words.

Example black <u>king</u> purple green <u>house</u>

1 long wide smart short fast

2 head ankle body leg smile

3 oak mud sand beech elm

4 river desert stream brook ocean

5 catch field haul meadow drag

5

Find the three-letter word which can be added to the letters in capitals to make a new word. The new word will complete the sentence sensibly.

Example The cat sprang onto the MO. <u>USE</u>

6 Please SHAR your pencil. _____

7 The lack of rain has caused a HOSEE ban. _____

8 We do ITION and subtraction in maths. _____

9 I had to SCH my room this morning when I couldn't find my homework. _____

10 The teacher asked the pupils to take out some PR and a pen. _____

5

Find the letter which will complete both pairs of words, ending the first word and starting the second. The same letter must be used for both pairs of words.

Example mea (<u>t</u>) able   fi (<u>t</u>) ub

11 ever (__) ellow   happ (__) ule

12 faste (__) uby   mise (__) oute

13 frigh (__) error   spa (__) able

14 rea (__) ise   pai (__) ound

15 fou (__) ight   cal (__) oad

5

Underline two words, one from each group, that go together to form a new word. The word in the first group always comes first.

Example (hand, <u>green</u>, for)   (light, <u>house</u>, sure)

16 (net, side, hat)   (ball, case, mug)

17 (flat, hard, big)   (room, age, mate)

18 (hit, tap, pat)　　　　(ten, tear, tern)

19 (poor, open, good)　　(can, door, will)

20 (car, fan, man)　　　　(ate, ear, age)

5

Find the four-letter word hidden at the end of one word and the beginning of the next word. The order of the letters may not be changed.

B 21

　　　Example　The children had bats and balls.　　*sand*

21 The king finished his speech by wishing everyone goodnight.　　_____

22 The old man enjoyed seeing his grandchildren.　　_____

23 The Pope arrived back at the Vatican late that night.　　_____

24 They sat under the umbrella and talked until the sun went down.　　_____

25 Clodagh was very brave in the hospital.　　_____

5

Move one letter from the first word and add it to the second word to make two new words.

B 13

　　　Example　hunt　sip　　*hut*　*snip*

26 shelf　　sell　　_____　_____

27 brown　shoe　　_____　_____

28 share　　mash　　_____　_____

29 crate　　pat　　_____　_____

30 least　　ton　　_____　_____

5

Find and underline the two words which need to change places for each sentence to make sense.

B 17

　　　Example　She went to <u>letter</u> the <u>write</u>.

31 When the wind blows the trees fall from the leaves.

32 He thought that he had come race in the first.

33 Please eat your bowl and clear away your breakfast.

34 The winner won a silver medal and the runner-up a gold one.

35 You have to find deep to dig the hidden treasure.

5

Fill in the missing letters. The alphabet has been written out to help you.

A B C D E F G H I J K L M N O P Q R S T U V W X Y Z

Example   AB is to CD as PQ is to RS

36 BR is to DT as FV is to _____

37 XU is to UR as TQ is to _____

38 PN is to TJ is to SQ is to _____

39 WA is to WB is to WC is to _____

40 MN is to LO as KP is to _____

Here are the number codes for five words. Match the right word to the right code.

PART	PANE	NEAR	PINE	NINE
2849	2528	3528	3491	3428

41 PART   _____

42 PANE   _____

43 PINE   _____

44 NEAR   _____

45 NINE   _____

Five children: Danny, Ella, Petra, Li and Sharif have pets. Petra has a goldfish and a hamster. Ella, Danny and Li have cats. Sharif, Li, Danny and Ella have dogs. Li does not like hamsters, but has a mouse.

46 Who has the most pets?   _____

47 Which pets does Danny have?   _____

48 Who only has a dog?   _____

49 In five years' time Annabelle will be 10.
    How old was she three years ago?   _____

50   In two years' time Jamie will be half the age of his sister,
     who is 12 now. How old is Jamie now?   _____

If D = 2, F = 4, H = 6, J = 12, and L = 24, give the answers to these calculations as letters.

51 D + D + D = _____

52 J − H = _____

53 D × D = _____

54 L ÷ J = _____

55 D × (H ÷ D) = _____

Change one word so that the sentence makes sense. Underline the word you are taking out and write your new word on the line.

B 14

Example   I waited in line to buy a <u>book</u> to see the film.   *ticket*

56 I went to the flower station to fill up my car for the long journey.   _____

57 Ellen took her sick hamster to the garage.   _____

58 The cat liked to sleep near the window to catch the
   last of the moon's rays.   _____

59 The swan stretched its graceful, long foot as it floated in the pond.   _____

60 My favourite sort of ice marshmallow is chocolate.   _____   **5**

Solve the problems by working out the letter codes. The alphabet has been written out to help you.

B 24

A B C D E F G H I J K L M N O P Q R S T U V W X Y Z

61 In a code, FASTER is written as IDVWHU. How would you write RATES? _____

62 In a code, SPORT is written as URQTV. How would you write PLUM?   _____

63 In a code, MOST is written as NQVX. What does TCOI stand for?   _____

64 In a code, BEAN is written as DCCL. What does UFQU stand for?   _____

65 In a code, CREST is written as FUHVW. How would you write MASK?   _____   **5**

Now go to the Progress Chart to record your score!   Total   **65**

Paper 13

Look at these groups of words.

B 1

A	B	C	D
beef	orange	water	potato
lamb	pear	lemonade	cabbage
pork	cherry	coffee	pea

Choose the correct group for each of the words below. Write in the letter.

1 lemon   _____

2 spinach   _____

3 tea   _____

4 chicken   _____

5 grape   _____   **5**

Underline the two words, one from each group, which are closest in meaning.

Example (race, shop, <u>start</u>) (finish, <u>begin</u>, end)

6 (old, patterned, hunt) (new, search, faint)

7 (similar, opposite, wide) (afar, last, alike)

8 (out, back, overtake) (pass, front, in)

9 (show, contain, hide) (display, cry, guess)

10 (clean, tidy, vague) (sunny, explained, unclear)

B 3

5

Underline one word in the brackets which is most opposite in meaning to the word in capitals.

Example WIDE (broad vague long <u>narrow</u> motorway)

11 FAIL (work point pass fade call)

12 PEACE (quiet softness old calm conflict)

13 REPAIR (fix push damage flatten paint)

14 LEAD (chase trail pant follow hound)

15 CERTAIN (sure absolute positive true doubtful)

B 6

5

Underline the one word in the brackets which will go equally well with both the pairs of words outside the brackets.

Example rush, attack cost, fee (price, hasten, strike, <u>charge</u>, money)

16 pot, tin able, willing (box, well, metal, can, agreeable)

17 delicate, weightless ignite, flare (light, heavy, hot, dim, flat)

18 smack, strike success, chart-topper (pat, stroke, winning, hit, put)

19 light, shining able, clever (fired, ablaze, bright, cunning, lively)

20 elegant, stylish hurt, ache (neat, painful, tidy, paranoid, smart)

B 5

5

Find a word that can be put in front of each of the following words to make new, compound words.

Example CAST FALL WARD POUR <u>DOWN</u>

21 HOUSE FLY GROCER FINCH _____

22 PECKER WORM CUTTER WIND _____

23 PLACE ARM FIGHTER SIDE _____

24 BAG SHAKE RAIL WRITING _____

25 BRUSH CUT BAND DRESSER _____

B 11

5

Find the four-letter word hidden at the end of one word and the beginning of the next word. The order of the letters may not be changed.

B 21

Example The children had bats and balls. <u>sand</u>

26 All the boys and girls played sensibly at break-time. _____

27 Alex was ready for his grand gala centenary celebrations. _____

28 The famous actor never once forgot her lines. _____

29 After my hard work, I was glad to have scored top in my class. _____

30 I usually read for thirty minutes before I go to bed. _____

5

Remove one letter from the word in capital letters to leave a new word. The meaning of the new word is given in the clue.

B 12

Example AUNT an insect <u>ant</u>

31 MEAN male _____

32 STORE painful _____

33 PILOT plan _____

34 SHOP jump _____

35 TRIP tear _____

5

Find and underline the two words which need to change places for each sentence to make sense.

B 17

Example She went to <u>letter</u> the <u>write</u>.

36 We put the cake in the bake to oven.

37 We put the names in alphabetical order so Bindy came before Annabel.

38 I sometimes count on my homework when doing my maths fingers.

39 The red rose is often white or wild in colour.

40 I have red seven pages in my read level book.

5

Find the letter which will end the first word and start the second word.

B 10

Example peac (<u>h</u>) ome

41 star (___) arth

42 cras (___) all

43 hai (___) ail

44 pac (___) ear

45 el (___) new

5

Here are the number codes for five words. Match the right word to the right code.

B 24

BOOT	FALL	ALTO	TOOL	BAIL
3297	5117	3115	8277	2751

46 BOOT _____

47 FALL _____

48 ALTO _____

49 TOOL _____

50 BAIL _____

5

Peter, David and Asif sit in a row in class. David is not beside Asif, who sits on the right of the three.

B 25

51 Who sits on the left? _____

52 Who is in the middle? _____

2

53 In six years' time Alice will be twice as old as her sister, who is two now. How old will Alice be? _____

B 25

54 Four years ago Robert was five. In five years' time he will be half the age of his brother. How old is his brother now? _____

55 Town A is south of town B, east of town D and west of town F. Town C is north-east of town A. Which town is furthest west? _____

3

Rearrange the letters in capitals to make another word. The new word has something to do with the first two words.

B 16

Example spot soil SAINT <u>STAIN</u>

56 twos doubles PARIS _____

57 goes out leaves EXIST _____

58 dressing gravy CAUSE _____

59 herb wise AGES _____

60 hazard risk GARDEN _____

5

Change one word so that the sentence makes sense. Underline the word you are taking out and write your new word on the line.

Example   I waited in line to buy a <u>book</u> to see the film.   _ticket_

61 The butcher had baked several cakes.   _____

62 Tame animals do not make very good pets.   _____

63 The bird had constructed a beautiful hole out of twigs.   _____

64 Sunday is the last month of the calendar year.   _____

65 The nurse asked her pupils to take their seats.   _____   **5**

Now go to the Progress Chart to record your score!   **Total**   **65**

Paper 14

Underline the pair of words most similar in meaning.

Example   come, go   <u>roam, wander</u>   fear, fare

1 hurry, rest   swift, fast   break, fix

2 back, rear   hold, tie   under, over

3 polish, dirty   hunt, dog   miniature, small

4 shoot, score   aim, goal   wind, wave

5 take, give   prize, present   pole, rod   **5**

Underline the pair of words most opposite in meaning.

Example   cup, mug   coffee, milk   <u>hot, cold</u>

6 wide, open   brilliant, dull   over, beyond

7 start, begin   fade, flatten   rude, polite

8 rise, fall   flake, drop   bounce, jump

9 post, join   criticise, praise cry, wail

10 relaxed, tense   teach, instruct   lose, misplace   **5**

Underline the one word in the brackets which will go equally well with both the pairs of words outside the brackets.

Example rush, attack   cost, fee   (price, hasten, strike, <u>charge</u>, money)

11 obvious, apparent   fields, grassland   (clear, plain, lawn, simple, ordinary)

12 elegance, beauty   prayer, thanks   (grace, amen, goodwill, attraction, power)

13 fill, arrange   bundle, parcel   (swell, gift, pack, place, pile)

14 particle, speck   cereal, seed   (piece, corn, bit, plant, grain)

15 sun, sky   celebrity, actor   (moon, star, shine, head, main)

5

Find the letter which will complete both pairs of words, ending the first word and starting the second. The same letter must be used for both pairs of words.

Example mea (<u>t</u>) able   fi (<u>t</u>) ub

16 star (___) ver   man (___) ntry

17 car (___) angy   hin (___) umble

18 sa (___) ame   ho (___) rink

19 plan (___) ill   hun (___) nit

20 sou (___) ale   ram (___) rove

5

Find the four-letter word hidden at the end of one word and the beginning of the next word. The order of the letters may not be changed.

Example The children had bats and balls.   _sand_

21 Who let the cat in?   _____

22 My dad's shed generally is rather messy.   _____

23 Tremors from a severe earthquake can end up many miles away.   _____

24 Fraser lent Sam a pencil because he'd left his at home.   _____

25 I understand that aspirin deadens pain in the back.   _____

5

Change the first word into the last word, by changing one letter at a time and making a new, different word in the middle.

Example CASE   _CASH_   LASH

26 PANT _____ PARK

27 MOST _____ MINT

28 SOUR _____ SEAR

29 BEAT _____ BRAG

30 NUTS _____ CATS

5

Look at the first group of three words. The word in the middle has been made from the other two words. Complete the second group of three words in the same way, making a new word in the middle of the group.

B 18

Example PAIN INTO TOOK   ALSO <u>SOON</u> ONLY

31 PALE   PEST   STIR   TAKE   ____   STOP

32 SOAR   OAST   TIME   SALE   ____   ONLY

33 FOOL   LOST   MAST   LEAP   ____   STAR

34 PRICE   RACE   PANIC   SPELT   ____   BISON

35 STEAM   LATE   CLEAR   TREND   ____   CREAM

Find the letter which will end the first word and start the second word.

B 10

Example peac (<u>h</u>) ome

36 caree (___) ent

37 fir (___) dge

38 car (___) here

39 fee (___) rack

40 lam (___) atten

Underline the two words, one from each group, which are closest in meaning.

B 3

Example (race, shop, <u>start</u>)   (finish, <u>begin</u>, end)

41 (pound, paint, wash)   (beat, drop, destroy)

42 (lower, move, turn)   (raise, reduce, tear)

43 (mould, attach, injure)   (damage, remove, subtract)

44 (game, sickness, pattern)   (repair, chess, illness)

45 (knotty, spoilt, tough)   (weak, blessed, strong)

Find a word that can be put in front of each of the following words to make a new, compound word.

B 11

Example CAST   FALL   WARD   POUR   <u>DOWN</u>

46 LOCK   FARE   LORD   PATH   _____

47 FOWL   FRONT   LOGGED COURSE   _____

48 PROOF   BOARD   MAN   VANE   _____

49 OVER   BOOK   PORT   WORD   _____

50 ACHE   SPACE   GROUND PACK   _____

Fill in the missing letters and numbers. The alphabet has been written out to help you.

A B C D E F G H I J K L M N O P Q R S T U V W X Y Z

Example CQ   DQ   EP   FP   <u>GO</u>   <u>HO</u>

51 AL   EL   IM   MM   _____   _____

52 AA   ZZ   BB   YY   _____   _____

53 ZX   XV   VT   TR   _____   _____

54 NM   NO   ON   OP   _____   _____

55 A1   C2   E3   G4   _____   _____

B 23

5

If ← ↑ → ↓ ↔ ϒ ↑ is the code for REPLACE, what do these codes stand for?

B 24

56 → ↑ ↔ ←   _____

57 ϒ ↓ ↔ →   _____

58 → ↔ ↓ ↑   _____

59 ↓ ↑ ↑ ←   _____

60 → ↔ ↓ ↔ ϒ ↑   _____

5

Change one word so that the sentence makes sense. Underline the word you are taking out and write your new word on the line.

B 14

Example I waited in line to buy a <u>book</u> to see the film.   *ticket*

61 Mrs Stokes found that a glass of warm milk helped her wake at night. _____

62 One of Roger's guitar notes broke as he practised. _____

63 After being fatally wounded, the soldier was pronounced alive when he reached the hospital. _____

64 Watching the moon rise is a wonderful way to start the morning. _____

65 I was so hungry because I ate all of my dinner and then had a second helping. _____

5

Now go to the Progress Chart to record your score!   **Total** 65

Paper 15

Underline the two words, one from each group, which are closest in meaning.

B 3

Example (race, shop, <u>start</u>)   (finish, <u>begin</u>, end)

1 (speak, take, ask)   (request, put, give)

2 (rough, shiny, clean)   (wild, glistening, dirty)

3 (destroyed, repaired, reformed)   (closed, compared, broken)

4 (cross, flighty, upset)   (angry, cheerful, pale)

5 (drum, stick, noise)   (tap, loud, music)   ◯ 5

Underline the two words, one from each group, which are the most opposite in meaning.   B 9

    Example   (dawn, <u>early</u>, wake)   (<u>late</u>, stop, sunrise)

6 (shy, old, late)   (aged, confident, true)

7 (cause, result, outcome)   (effect, mistake, hide)

8 (follow, collect, light)   (win, heavy, succeed)

9 (tired, controlled, hungry)   (starving, thirsty, energetic)

10 (numb, hurting, rare)   (painful, common, protected)   ◯ 5

Find the letter which will end the first word and start the second word.   B 10

    Example   peac (<u>h</u>) ome

11 pai (___) ule

12 fi (___) ase

13 too (___) ast

14 cove (___) ain

15 pun (___) oung   ◯ 5

Find the four-letter word hidden at the end of one word and the beginning of the next word. The order of the letters may not be changed.   B 21

    Example   The children had bats and balls.   <u>*sand*</u>

16 You are lucky as it is the final one in the shop.   _____

17 He considered the cash unnecessary in the circumstances.   _____

18 The Incas taught us many interesting things.   _____

19 The crowd quit cheering when the team lost the ball.   _____

20 He ate the bag of sweets himself.   _____   ◯ 5

Which one letter can be added to the front of all these words to make new words?   B 12

    Example   <u>c</u>are   <u>c</u>at   <u>c</u>rate   <u>c</u>all

21 ___reak   ___rand   ___all   ___oat

22 ___oat   ___ool   ___lean   ___hain

23 ___ake   ___orn   ___oad   ___urn

24 ___ir   ___ate   ___ind   ___ault

25 ___ind   ___est   ___ould   ___hite

5

Remove one letter from the word in capital letters to leave a new word. The meaning of the new word is given in the clue.

B 12

Example   AUNT   an insect   _ant_

26 DRAGOON   mythical beast   _____

27 COVER   bay   _____

28 ORATION   limited amount   _____

29 SHINE   leg   _____

30 METEOR   measuring instrument   _____

5

Find and underline the two words which need to change places for each sentence to make sense.

B 17

Example   She went to <u>letter</u> the <u>write</u>.

31 The old track chugged along the endless train.

32 England is one of the largest counties in Kent.

33 I really enjoy classical films and black and white music.

34 It was very home so I ran briskly late.

35 The house was delivered to the wrong newspaper by mistake.

5

Choose two words, one from each set of brackets, to complete the sentences in the best way.

B 15

Example   Tall is to (tree, <u>short</u>, colour) as narrow is to (thin, white, <u>wide</u>).

36 Speedy is to (fast, slow, late) as low is to (last, high, calm).

37 Ignore is to (overlook, welcome, accept) as praise is to (forget, change, honour).

38 Well is to (water, ill, better) as mine is to (wood, coal, wheat).

39 Damp is to (wet, sandy, dry) as cool is to (snow, rain, cold).

40 Kite is to (fly, sky, bird) as badger is to (nest, zoo, mammal).

5

If A = 1, B = 4, D = 5, E = 10, S = 20, what are the sums of the following words by adding the letters together?

41 BAD = _____

42 SEED = _____

Give the answer to these calculations as letters.

43 S – E = _____

44 (A + B) + D = _____

45 E – D = _____

Find the letter which will complete both pairs of words, ending the first word and starting the second. The same letter must be used for both pairs of words.

Example   mea (t̠) able   fi (t̠) ub

46 clai (___) ost   cal (___) en

47 pra (___) olk   tr (___) oung

48 pac (___) nd   craz (___) ase

49 bal (___) ose   foo (___) eck

50 ful (___) oot   scraw (___) and

Rearrange the letters in capitals to make another word. The new word has something to do with the first two words.

Example   spot   soil   SAINT   STAIN

51 jump   hop   PALE   _____

52 untrue   unreal   FLEAS   _____

53 not strong   fragile   WAKE   _____

54 annoys   upsets   RANGES   _____

55 fruit   canteloupe   LEMON   _____

Change the first word into the last word, by changing one letter at a time and making a new, different word in the middle.

Example   CASE   CASH   LASH

56 POST _____ PACT

57 MICE _____ MATE

58 ARTS _____ AIMS

59 SHIP _____ SNAP

60 FLOW _____ FLAT

Fill in the missing letters and numbers. The alphabet has been written out to help you.

A B C D E F G H I J K L M N O P Q R S T U V W X Y Z

Example   AB is to CD as PQ is to RS

61 DN is to BL as GQ is to _____

62 BB is to YY as DD is to _____

63 JJ is to LM as QQ is to _____

64 ZY is to ZX as ZW is to _____

65 A1 is to B2 as Y25 is to _____

5

Now go to the Progress Chart to record your score!   Total   65

Progress Chart   Verbal Reasoning 9-10 years Book 2

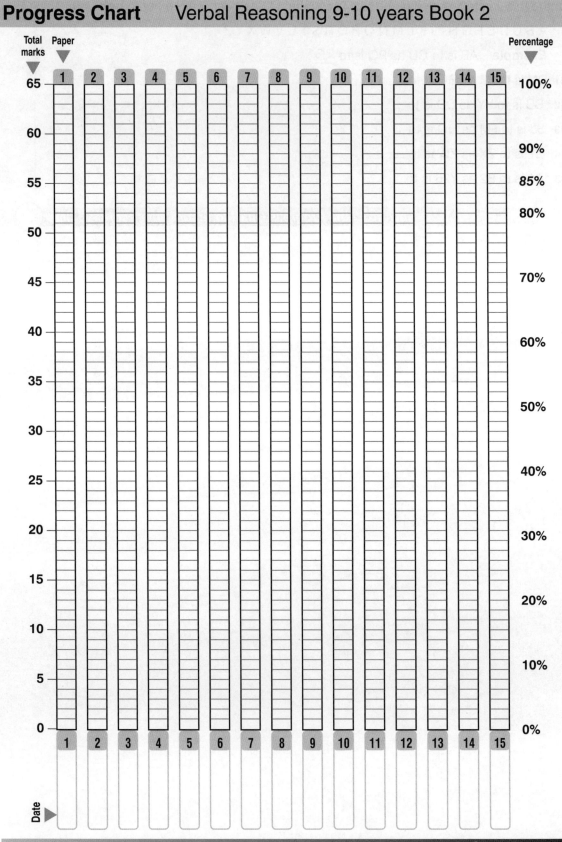

When you've finished the book use the Next Steps Planner